AN UNLESSONED GIRL

Margaret Maddocks' novels

Margaret Maddocks

An Unlessoned Girl

With drawings by
Margaret Wetherbee

Hutchinson of London

Hutchinson & Co (Publishers) Ltd
3 Fitzroy Square, London W1

London Melbourne Sydney Auckland
Wellington Johannesburg and agencies
throughout the world

First published in 1977
© Margaret Maddocks 1977
Drawings © Hutchinson & Co (Publishers) Ltd 1977
Set in Monotype Baskerville

Printed in Great Britain by
The Anchor Press Ltd and bound by
Wm Brendon & Son Ltd
both of Tiptree, Essex

ISBN 0 09 128520 8

To Jack

Acknowledgements

The author would like to thank the following for their
kind permission to quote from copyright material:
Sir John Betjeman: *Middlesex* and *Baker Street Station* from
    Collected Poems
Jonathan Cape Ltd:
On behalf of the Executors of the Estate of C. Day Lewis:
    The Album by C. Day Lewis, from *Collected Poems 1954*
    printed by the Hogarth Press
Together with the Society of Authors, literary representatives
    of the Estate of A. E. Housman: *A Shropshire Lad* by A. E.
    Housman, from *Collected Poems*
J. M. Dent & Sons Ltd together with the Trustees of the
    Estate of Dylan Thomas: *Do not go gentle into that good
    night,* from *Collected Poems of Dylan Thomas*
Faber & Faber Ltd: *The Sunlight on the Garden* by Louis
    MacNeice, from *Collected Poems*
Macmillan Ltd: *The Old Ladies* by Colin Ellis, from
    Mournful Numbers
The Society of Authors, literary representatives of the
    Estate of John Masefield: *An Epilogue* by John Masefield.

An unlesson'd girl, unschool'd, unpractised:
Happy in this, she is not yet so old
But she may learn.

Shakespeare, The Merchant of Venice

Before the Climb

I

The sunlight on the garden
Hardens and grows cold,
We cannot cage the minute
Within its nets of gold,
When all is told
We cannot beg for pardon.

Louis MacNeice

Whenever my grandmother went out her daughters were required to re-trim her hat but as her excursions seldom numbered more than three a year, such a procedure was not so excessive as it sounds. These journeys had to be within the radius of a horse's capacity, for she went, as she said, 'In Pierce.' Pierce, a man with a blue face faintly lined in red and wearing an ancient green livery, surmounted by a top hat, kept a carriage which he plied for hire and drove himself. 'Young' Pierce had lately acquired what my grandmother called a motor and this met us at the station, but for her own visitations she patronized his father. Her most important outing took place in August, when we were staying with her, a time considered both suitable and convenient for a round of ceremonial calls.

As Pierce was always late and my grandmother was always early, there was what seemed to me – old enough to accompany her and already uncomfortable in my best dress and hat – an interminable wait before the ecstasy of the drive could begin. Once indeed, on a never-to-be-forgotten occasion, which made him even more distrusted, he forgot us altogether and without a handy telephone it was a whole day before the matter could be cleared up and a week before the complications of anxious waiting hostesses, unexplained broken appointments, sumptuous unattended teas could be sorted out by frantic correspondence and it was months before my grandmother recovered.

It would be wrong to give the impression that she never had a really new hat, for she did. Every time there was a wedding (and in that house there were seven) a monumental confection of flowers and tulle and straw and veiling, with perhaps a little fruit, was bought. It appeared in the photographs of wedding groups which adorned the bedroom walls; faded beige records of dead great-aunts and uncles and here and there our own mother as a child bridesmaid, pensive over a basket of flowers. Our bearded grandfather was there too and bridegrooms with twirling moustaches; anxious brides watching for the birdie; all were preserved for posterity and in the centre, the organizer of the feast, was my grandmother, her face kind but serious under her latest hat.

As soon as the visits had been fixed and Pierce had been ordered, a box containing a fascinating collection of trimmings, saved from former finery, was brought out and turned over by the three daughters, watched by me. My mother, having migrated to London, would be the arbiter of taste and fashion. Rose would smile approval, but it was Lily, the middle one, who did the work. Eventually, after numerous try-outs before the old mirror and obedient murmurs of approval from my grandfather behind his newspaper, the latest hat would be pronounced as good as four women and one small girl could make it.

Now the only worry was the weather, for if it rained the carriage would have to be shut and we must spend the afternoon in a stuffy box, which smelt of horse and straw, my grandmother's eau de cologne and my Pears' soap. Pears' soap is supposed to be unscented, nevertheless its smell, which was really a lack of smell, just unadulterated refreshing cleanliness, permeated all important occasions of my childhood.

In an agony of apprehension we waited for Pierce. At intervals my grandmother took out her gold-chased fob watch and shook it. It was seldom used and thus neglected and maltreated it was given to stopping at dramatic and inconvenient moments. She then gazed despairingly through her veil at the clock, which was purposely kept fast, but as no one knew exactly how fast one could only make an approximate guess at the time, for whenever my grandmother passed it she was in the habit of pushing on the hands a few minutes, in the hope of making her dilatory daughters aware of the time.

My father, in affectionate irritation at the peculiarities of the family into which he had married, said one might as well take a bearing from the Pole Star.

Now as we waited for Pierce, the minutes ticked by on the big clock with the mirror behind it, just like the picture in *Alice Through the Looking Glass*. The hour would arrive and then it would pass. Still we waited – the tension was almost unbearable. In the hope of conjuring Pierce out of the air I would be sent to the gate to keep watch.

He could be heard before he was actually seen, as he jerked his horse up the steepness of the lane's beginnings when it left the main road, through the dust, between the hedges, and then, suddenly, there he was at the bend, bumping over the ruts about which my grandfather complained for forty years and after he died his daughter Lily continued the fight, for the road to the little green and the handful of houses in the Worcestershire hamlet where my grandparents lived was 'unadopted'. A drunken notice at the corner said so. I used to picture it, fatherless and motherless, lonely and unwanted, with only us to love it.

Pierce was now reported to be in sight; every moment brought him nearer and at last there was this indescribable sound – a clip-clop – a rattle of wheels – a scrunch. It seemed as if the long-drawn-out 'Ah – ah – ah!', which he gave as he drew up, swept away all our worries. My socks would be tugged into place by my mother, my hat straightened by my aunt, my gloves were found. It was ascertained that I had an accessible handkerchief. Discreetly someone made sure I had 'been'. I was told I must be good. The basket of plums for Mrs Lea and the box of apples for Miss Knott were stowed away under my feet in a tantalizing manner, because I could not be given one in case I damaged the virgin whiteness of my clothes. We waved as if we were off to America, solemn and excited at the imminence of a change. When my mother and my aunts stood at the gate watching us turn round the green and drive off down the lane in Pierce, the grandeur of the carriage overcame me. I should not have been surprised if my grandmother, resplendent in her refurbished hat, had acknowledged the cheers of the crowd, like the Queen.

'I hope we don't look hired,' I said.

On these occasions I accompanied my grandmother mainly for the ride. Having only seldom access to a means of transport other than my own skinny legs, a ride in anything with wheels was undreamt-of bliss. Jack, the old horse which had drawn my grandfather's wagonette, had been commandeered to fight the Germans. I pictured terrible monsters in spiked helmets personally dragging our dear old pet away, to be part of a composite imagining, based on an engraving in the hall, of the Battle of Sebastopol. The fact that the old horse's name was the same as my brother's made the incident I conjured out of the grown-ups' indignation even more moving. Now the wagonette remained in the coach-house, shafts down, forsaken and dejected, demoted from an object we were forbidden to touch to a plaything for a wet day.

A friend of my grandmother's had a governess cart, and when she called on her way back from a trip into Worcester, she would be given sherry and biscuits and we would wait around in the hope of being taken for a short way down the Malvern Road and over the Old Bridge. Here we would alight and thank her with a polite kiss which tasted of her veil, thinking the walk home, along the short cut made by the hopyard and up a steep path through brambles and nettles, well worth the effort. When we visited a cousin who had married a farmer I would stand proud as Boadicea in the milk float driven by his carter, who had the reins wound round a hook which took the place of his hand in an awe-inspiring manner, and sometimes, on memorable occasions, when we were walking back from church, we would be overtaken by a neighbour's car and given a lift. This was rare for few people had such luxuries, least of all the friends of my grandparents.

There was, of course, always the tram.

This ran from the Cross in Worcester to the suburb of St John's and after that there was a long weary trek along the road which my grandfather called the Turnpike; then up an interminable footpath between hedges to Lower Wick, in those days an isolated collection of old houses round a little green. The tram was such an adventure (if one rode on the top, that is; inside it merely made one sick), that the walk to the terminus on the Malvern Road was undertaken with enthusiastic bounds. The return walk, even after an ice-cream at the Cathedral Café, was another matter. Burdened as we were with the shopping, it was liable to feel like an endurance test, but when the twin poplars and our grandparents' chimneys appeared on the horizon we were spurred on by thoughts of a gigantic meal, second helpings of everything, pies and puddings of vast dimensions, laughter and gentle teasing.

It was a long dining-table, for we were often ten or more. Lily sat at one end and my grandfather always took his place next to my grandmother, who presided at the other end. However many we were he would never be parted from her. She it was who carved, doing it so badly that my perfectionist of a father at her side could scarcely control his cries of horror.

'Show me, then,' she said one day, and this he did with the touch of the surgeon he had always wanted to be, and as we watched we grew in time to know how to sever a chicken's legs and the exact point of the wing joint; where to plunge the knife into a leg of lamb, when to turn the shoulder over. While my father was there he came gradually to carve, for he had a way of being in charge, even in his mother-in-law's house. He loved her better than his own mother, who, though a sterling character, was altogether more formidable. His wife's mother was generous and forbearing, kind and rather overweight, a comfortable woman, capable and practical, not what she would have called 'clever'. But she was easy to love and when she lay dying both her sons-in-law burst into tears as they walked over the familiar mat.

'They were useless, the two of them,' said Lily, years afterwards. 'Absolutely useless,' confirming her still held scorn of everything male, except her own father.

'Men!' she sniffed, for of course she it was who had arranged the funeral. She was the one who nursed devotedly when required, worked hard with no labour-saving devices, gave up her dreams to live at home, sang in a sweet husky voice in the choir, always a little breathless from hurrying most of the way. It was Lily who balanced the meagre budgets so that no one noticed or even cared how little money was there to spend. She had a poor opinion of her fellow human beings, particularly a composite scapegoat called 'Government', and looking back over the years one cannot be surprised that her opinion at ninety-four has remained unchanged.

Lily always wanted to be a nurse but, except for a brief spell as a VAD in the First World War, this ambition was unrealized, because she considered it her duty to remain at home, and duty, for her, was one four-letter word frequently on her lips. However, her skills were seldom out of use. When she was over eighty she was still on call for every family emergency and one of my earliest memories is of her comforting hand on my head, while I made the most of an attack of whooping cough. I am ashamed to say that as a child I loved her less than the other grown-ups, who came and went in that hospitable house, and I was much older before I learnt to appreciate her. She gave us stern uplifting lectures and took life seriously. No one else appeared to do this. Everything seemed to have a background of laughter. Rose, the youngest of the three daughters, had a soft, infectious giggle, which was a god-send to any would-be comic. My grandfather was a poker-faced joker while my father's wit, which at home sometimes had a cutting edge, became, like everything else at Wick, sometimes unbearably funny. With our noses barely four inches from the trough we children would fall about with laughter until Lily brought us back to reality by warning us that if we laughed before breakfast we would cry before night, and that one laughed before one cried. Even these gloomy predictions did not stop us. I suppose I must have shed some tears in that house, for I cried easily and often, hurt where no hurt was meant, and sometimes burdened by deep fears and secret terrors, but only the sound of laughter remains, perhaps helped by Uncle Willie's Little Jokes.

Willie married Rose when she was nearly thirty and he was not far off fifty. They were ideally suited, both being uncomplicated, good-tempered souls, devoid of the ambitions which drove our father, busy seeking his fortune in London, into prodigies of work and further study, in the determination that the eldest daughter, whom he had taken away, should be compensated.

'Work,' Uncle Willie declared, 'is only for fools and carthorses.'

This to my father was stark heresy and it was hoped we would not take in the oft-repeated maxim. But we did. They are the only words of my kindly little uncle which remain. His jokes, however, none of us can ever forget, for one of the excitements of his arrival was to see what the proprietor of the joke shop had been able to sell him. Long after the initial surprise of the telescope which ringed the eyes with soot, the chocolates which were glued to the box, the cigarettes which came out on a long string, had all lost their first hilarious impact, we would continue to play with them and to the end of time they were all used on any unsuspecting stranger. Indeed I have some of them yet. But the cushion which made an embarrassing noise was taken away.

It was, we were informed, rude.

2

The past slides out of its leaves to haunt me.

C. Day Lewis

My grandmother's father, William Goodwin, died as the result of a hunting accident, leaving a widow of forty and his eldest daughter's lasting fear of horses.

He came from a long line of millers going back many hundreds of years, hard-headed, hard-riding, hard-working men, successful and independent. It would appear that they were also virile, one of them having by means of two wives produced no less than twenty-two children, so the ramification of cousins, first, second and third, removed and removed yet again, was prodigious. If someone with the Goodwin name and looks turned up in the news, my grandmother would say, 'Must be one of T.K.'s.' He was Mayor of Worcester three times and when he went to London, for a reason unknown, to meet the Emperor of France, Louis Napoleon told him he was a typical John Bull, as indeed his portrait shows. With much re-telling and faulty memories most of the family stories became laced with fantasy, but we believed them all.

My great-grandmother, who died a few years before I was born, was left moderately well off, and this she needed to be for, besides my grandmother, she had six other children. These she managed to bring up, sending them to boarding schools and starting them off in life. She came to live with my grandparents soon after they married and was a stern memory of my mother's childhood; Lily and Rose would entertain us endlessly with stories about her. She never went to bed until one of the children had looked under it for a possible intruder. Being a handsome woman, perhaps she was disappointed when, after a terrified peek, they pronounced the All Clear. Her husband also had been, it is said, extremely handsome and these good looks persisted in various branches of that prolific family.

From this long line of independent men of business, who owed no man, my grandmother, having inherited a modest sum from her father, married into a family of light-hearted spenders. Against her better judgment, but because it was thought right, some of the little she had was lent to stave off the bankruptcy of her improvident in-laws and remained a controversial source of resentment. Long before I was born she had to 'manage' and 'manage' she did, how indeed one will never know. There was always a meal for the stranger, a mug of home-brewed cider at the back door, sherry and biscuits at the front.

'Give a penny, spend a penny and a penny save' was her oft-repeated motto as she put small sums into little boxes to accumulate, so that she could give us Christmas and birthday presents. Yet she never talked of money. As children we had no idea that it was scarce, for the things which it cannot buy were never in short supply; and like the sturdy stock from which she sprang, she never owed a halfpenny.

Because her widowed mother was living with her she, as eldest daughter, was the focal point of all the spreading branches of her numerous kin. At any moment the gate would squeak and in they came. Though rambling and inconvenient, her house was not large and I have often wondered where they all fitted in. They came for weddings and christenings and finally for funerals, voluble, overpowering and handsome. They came to recuperate from illnesses and some of them came there to die; fair, blue-eyed and tall, mostly, although when one of them married an Italian, darker, smaller beauties were produced.

Unfortunately, my father, by marrying my mother, brought down the average.

'The boy has our looks,' my grandmother would proudly say of my brother Jack. 'It's such a pity the girl takes after her father.'

'Do you get used to being plain?' I asked my father's youngest sister, whom I was supposed to resemble. She laughed and told me that the only consolation about being plain was that when you were old no one accused you of 'going off'. I was not consoled but I accepted the situation with a degree of stoicism. My single beauty, my hair, was no source of pleasure. It had to be washed (soap in the eyes), brushed, curled in sleep-disturbing rags, lugged from the head by the roots when the tangles were combed out, plaited into two long plaits and tied with ribbon. One of its more devastating hazards was that its silky fineness shed these adornments, and they were for ever being lost. For a moment, until my grandmother produced a new ribbon out of the same treasure-house of finery which trimmed her hats, I would be in disgrace. All the other girls had short hair, newly fashionable, but as my own fair ropes were supposed to be my only beauty, cutting them off was not considered. Of course no one ever gave me this reason, praise being considered sinful and liable to induce vanity. My father would playfully tug my plaits as I passed, but he resisted all arguments to have them cut off, even when my mother added her pleas. Such was the discipline of his ban that to disobey him did not occur to me and I was eighteen before he could be persuaded. I came back from the hairdresser's, shorn and marcel-waved and feeling like Helen of Troy, when to my absolute terror my father burst into tears and rushed from the house. It was the first time I had seen any of my elders actually cry, as so often overcome by the miseries of life I also cried, and it had never entered my head that they might have feelings too.

My grandmother did not believe in praise either. It was never given even if it was deserved and in my case it seldom was. I was adventurous, imaginative and naughty, permanently bandaged and scarred, and much given to arguing. This was deplored and known as 'answering back'. Reminded with frequency of our shortcomings, by rights we should have been miserable as children and neurotic as adults. Yet we were happy, more than that, at our grandmother's we were blissful. The wisdom of Freud and Spock was denied her. It was simply her nature to love us.

3

In my own shire if I was sad,
Homely comforters I had.

A. E. Housman

My grandfather's family only resembled the prolific hand-some brood of my grandmother's kin in that they all had their roots deeply embedded in Worcestershire. Although they had scarcely a cent between them, his relations were also proud of their ancestry, but theirs, they declared, went back to no less than one of the knights who came over with William the Conqueror. This unlikely ancestor brought us the name of Avern, said to be a corruption of Auvergne, and we were led to believe that a large portion of land in the next county had been given to him by his royal master, making us, in some unspecified manner, the rightful owners of the Edgbaston Cricket Field. There was dark talk of Money in Chancery and just before I was born, one American cousin did try to find this, but gave up, owing to the cost of the proceedings. However, such spendthrifts were they all, that if the story were true and they had been given most of Birmingham, the proceeds would have slipped incompre-hensibly through their fingers.

My grandmother, whose feet were firmly on the ground, found her in-laws occasionally trying and their tales of past grandeurs tiresome.

'They are proud,' she would say, giving the word its old meaning.

The kin of my grandfather's side also came to the house at Lower Wick. They were not so numerous as his in-laws, who used his house as their home; they came less often and they were absolutely different. My grandmother's relatives were all hearty, handsome and exuberant. 'Gay', like 'proud', is another word in our permissive society which has been debased and given a different meaning but 'gay' in the old sense describes my grandfather's kin and there is no word which has been invented to take its place. If they were 'proud' in the old sense they were also 'gay'. They were witty, full of pithy, ironic stories of anything ridiculous which caught their fancy. They were smaller, less obviously good-looking and, like the old comedians, something always happened to them on their way to the theatre. Cousin Edith could make me laugh to the day she died a few years ago, at the age of ninety-six. Her memory had gone so that she was not sure who I was and mixed me continually with my mother. I had not the heart to remind her that my mother, the playmate of her youth, was long dead.

What did they do, these light-hearted spenders so despised by my grandmother? Always inclined to extravagance and generosity they entertained lavishly, putting off the day of reckoning as long as they could. None of them was wild or vicious. They simply enjoyed themselves and were, because of their genes and their upbringing, apparently incapable of living within their means. They were chronic mismanagers, with no idea of simple budgeting.

Except that my grandfather had no money to mismanage, he might well have behaved in the same way but his modest finances were administered by his wife and Lily, and Lily mismanaged nothing, not even her parents, for into this extravagant strain her maternal forbears had injected prudence and a horror of unpaid bills.

The extravagance of her husband's relations never ceased to annoy my grandmother and Lily and Rose, but my mother, I suspect, was rather proud of them. Anonymous in un-friendly London, she would tell us about bygone glories, giving them an interest which, though founded on fact, may well have been embellished by romance. I wish now that I had listened with more attention and also that I had persevered to verify the stories.

25

This much I know to be true.

My grandfather was born in 1851 – the sixth and last child of his parents – at The Hill House, Great Witley, which his forbears had certainly occupied since 1743 and probably before that in another house on a site nearby, the ruins of which still remain. It lies on a small rise above a little reedy lake, sheltered by the hills of Abberley, its views serene and beautiful. It is reached from the road to Stourport by a long unmarked lane, so that it is difficult to find and when found it has a secret air.

In 1959 John, the son of Rose, and I were determined to seek it out and we made some unsuccessful searches until, at last, we reached a sudden end to a track and there we were at a stranger's back door with no excuse but curiosity. Embarrassed we quickly turned in the stable-yard and drove away before we were discovered. But the house imprinted itself on my consciousness and it became the setting for *Larksbrook*, the first of my novels to win an award and the beginning of a modest success. Based on such a brief look the interior had to be fantasy and the monkey puzzle, depicted by the artist, Margaret Wetherbee, on the cover of the book, was transplanted by my imagination from the lawn of my grandparents' house in Lower Wick. Until it blew down it was a landmark in the neighbourhood. Thus, in a strange way, I must have tried to capture the combined ambience of something which was gone but which had left lasting traces.

A few years after the publication of the book the kind owners of The Hill House, on hearing that we wished to see it, showed Jack and me over it. Except for the plumbing and lighting it is scarcely changed since the day my grandfather's family left it in 1852 and although I had never been inside, nothing surprised me. It was just as I had pictured it and described it, as if, in the back of my mind, I had always known the light, airy rooms, the beautiful turn of the staircase, the view across the valley from the windows.

Here the young mother of my grandfather had died, leaving him a baby and five older children. I had always assumed that she had died in childbirth but when I asked

Lily if she knew any details she said tersely, 'Of a broken heart I should think.' How true this is who can know? Her husband was in debt when he married her and had dissipated her not inconsiderable fortune. On her death he went abroad and later he also died. The five older children were taken care of by a relative and my grandfather was brought up in the village by his nurse. That, for the family, was the end of life at The Hill House.

The man who made himself responsible for them was a cousin called Pickernell, the squire of a neighbouring parish. He lived at Holt Castle, not a castle in the accepted sense, probably a fortified house, standing above the river Teme. It is now a block of flats. Here in some luxury Joseph, Thomas, Jane, Anne and Elizabeth were brought up. Thus they were all reared with ideas still above their means, for they obviously had little of their own and the bachelor squire must have been a good man indeed to have brought them this far.

The penniless family had to earn their own livings and their kind benefactor started them in the world. Thomas was sent to Paris to learn the finer aspects of milling. I suppose this must have been something suggested by my grandmother's family, who lived nearby and were friends. He died when I was small but I can just remember him, bottle-nosed, amusing, generous and permanently broke. Joseph, the eldest, died before I was born. He had been set up in an old established seed merchant's business in Worcester with a large nursery attached to it, situated in what was then country. It would seem he knew little about the enterprise and as he married a pretty, whist-loving, party-giving, wife, what he earned was easily spent.

Jane married and moved to live on the other side of the county but for Elizabeth the fate of a spinster was inevitable and she became the poor relation-cum-companion of a cousin.

Her sister Anne went to Italy, also as a companion to a young woman who fancied herself as a poet. At intervals privately bound books of her friend's poems were sent to my grandfather but after the First World War there was silence and Anne's name was never mentioned. One day recently I enquired as to her fate. From Lily's uncompromising expression I thought it must have been worse than death. But no, it was obviously even more terrible.

'We think,' Lily said, 'that she went over to Rome.'

My grandfather, left in the care of his nurse, was thus brought up in a different way from his siblings. Yet they kept in touch with their baby brother enough to set him slightly apart from his companions, but in such a way that he grew up with a simplicity of manner and a grace of bearing which endeared him to everyone. He was an attractive child with dark curly hair and blue eyes. One of his great-grandmothers had been Kitty Delaney of County Cork and he was the only one of the family who had inherited this undoubted Irish look. His eyes had an engaging sparkle, part innocence, part good humour.

This good-looking, intelligent boy, seemingly neglected in the simplicity of his upbringing, attracted the attention of various friends of his dead parents, including Lord Dudley, the old ironmaster who lived at Witley Court and because of his obvious knowledge and love of all growing things, he was sent as a youth to Kew, where he did well and made friends with Sir Joseph Hooker, the great naturalist. From his years there he emerged a highly trained horticulturalist – a gardener – and he joined his brother Joseph's enterprise. My grandfather, being the one with the knowledge, was put in charge of the nurseries and there, to the end of his days, he remained, becoming, as time passed, an expert in a wide field.

He wrote occasional articles, gave considered opinions when asked, advised in the development of parks, judged at shows. Today, with his charm of manner and bearing, his articulate explanations, his humour and artistic sense, and above all his immense and wide knowledge of his subjects, he would surely have been a television natural. In those days he merely became a character, so widely known that he was a landmark.

Because he looked so young at twenty-one he had grown a beard, at that time unusual, for shaven chins had become the fashion. It was curly and well-trimmed and started low enough to show the cleft in his chin (which we have all inherited) below a well-shaped humorous mouth. I never saw him lose his temper. My grandmother did not lose hers either but her lips would close in a firm line and she would take a deep breath to suppress her anger; one was aware that it was there. My grandfather merely gave A Look, made more meaningful by his beard, but even in this Look there was a hint of understanding, for he was a man who found condemnation difficult and his tolerance was the quality stressed in all his obituaries.

Like his eldest daughter, who became our mother, he suffered fools gladly. In some strange way they both saw into other people's minds and were ready to give them the benefit of the doubt.

His friends came from far and wide and from every walk in life. Once when he visited us in London his first port of call was number ten, Downing Street. My father tried to hint that the Prime Minister might be busy.

'Stanley will have time for me,' said my grandfather. 'We are friends.'

Stanley Baldwin might be Prime Minister but he was a fellow countryman and moreover a man of Worcestershire. Of course he was a friend.

None the less my grandfather was a dedicated Liberal and so was his daughter, Lily – though my father always insisted that they were both the most Conservative Liberals he had ever encountered. Lily was the daughter who was the closest to him, taking the place of the son he never had and giving up her life to caring for her parents.

Because of the isolation of his orphaned childhood, his wife and family were his chosen world and he even welcomed his widowed mother-in-law with open arms when she came to live with them until she died fifteen years later, accepting her in place of the mother he could not remember, loving her with more devotion than her own children and entertaining all her tribe of relatives with a friendly smile. But occasionally he talked of his own people. His grandmother had been a 'Miss-Hill-of-the-Hoo', he told me and one of his cousins was the famous Sir Rowland Hill, founder of the Penny Post. Another cousin, the Rector of Shellesley, was a contributor to *Punch*, and had written a novel called *Verdant Green*, a best seller of its day, under the name of Cuthbert Bede; Thackeray and Mark Lemon had been his friends. There was also a Dr Bradley, another cousin, who wrote long articles in *Berrow's Worcester Journal*, pages of old-fashioned type, looking as if it had been done with the John Bull printing set we had been given for Christmas. Grandfather had cut these out and saved them and we found them long afterwards when the house was given up. We found also galley proofs adorned with the symbols which I came to use in correcting my own novels, the itching pen being apparently as much inherited as the itching purse. We knew little about these people and had not the wit to probe further or listen more attentively to his tales. Sometimes we visited his relations who seemed to us to live in some splendour. One had his own race course and one a small private zoo.

In their houses were beautiful possessions, silver and pictures and furniture, which had been handed down over the generations. He did not seem to resent that almost nothing of this came to him. His greatest treasure was a sheet of paper on which a prayer had been copied. In his copperplate hand he had marked it, 'This is all I have which was written by my mother.' His brothers and sisters saved some things from the sale rooms but over the years most of it was sold except for a few family portraits and some silver candlesticks made to illuminate The Hill House for the Coronation of George the Fourth. Gradually it all vanished until the sole relics of this supposed grandeur were two small cannon which came, how, one asks oneself, from the Battle of Balaclava. Was this also one of the myths? They had at one time lent tone to the terrace of Holt Castle. From there they were somehow rescued by my grandfather's brother and partner, Joseph. They were fired, letting off startling pops and a good deal of smoke, on such joyful occasions as our parents' marriage, our births and comings of age. My father maintained that even the blanks were lethal, not only for anyone within range but for the dearly loved character who courageously fired them. He used to look after the horses, but now that there was none, in an ancient bowler hat he busied himself with the pigs. His cry rang out, 'Stand well back!' so we did. They were fired at the end of World War One but by the end of World War Two they had gone to help make other guns

From my grandfather's tales I realize that his forbears were like the characters of Trollopian novels. Impecunious, they found it necessary to marry money to preserve the position they thought was rightfully theirs and when they had worked through the fortunes of their wives, their heirs were forced to repeat the performance. A pattern was established until it gradually came to an end and all that remained were stories of days that were gone. Yet he was strangely content. He enjoyed his work and he enjoyed life so that there was no difference between the two. In precise, correct English, only faintly overlaid by the burr of Worcestershire, he spoke with the same charm to his pigman or the Prince of Wales. All the world was his friend.

To the end, in his early seventies, he remained slim and active, his hair still dark and thick, as he climbed with us up the Malvern Hills with no sign of breathlessness, until a careless motor-cyclist knocked him down and from this accident he did not properly recover. He still referred to the main road as 'The Turnpike' and, used to easier days, he was always a reckless jay walker. His life style had been different from that of his relations but he had enjoyed over fifty years of happy marriage, mostly in the house in which he died and he provided for his wife and Lily to continue their modest life there unchanged. His name was given to a rose and when the land was sold (without anyone realizing it was a potential gold mine, so that it went for very little) a road was named after him. He has his own immortality and he is still remembered.

When he died I was twenty, and I tried to tell my grandmother how sorry I was for her.

31

'It's a good thing I didn't go first,' she said, stroking my hand, as she always did when I was what she called 'in a state'. 'Without me he would have been lost.'

And I knew she was speaking the truth.

4

An unlesson'd girl, unschool'd, unpractised:
Happy in this, she is not yet so old
But she may learn.
            Shakespeare,The Merchant of Venice

When we arrived, at the familiar squeak of the gate, everyone would pour out of the house, a composite medley of friends and relations. To the stranger we were introduced as the grandchildren from London, and this instantly set us apart. Compared with the others we might have come from Mars. We would be hugged and told how we had grown and then we immediately escaped between our elders' legs to a corner of the dining-room, where the apples were piled in the big Royal Worcester dish. It was part of the bliss of our visit that we could help ourselves in passing without rebuke. When it was empty it was refilled, if not with apples then with pears or plums. Did we have colic? I do not remember. If greed were justly punished we should have died in agony. With a store of fruit we made straight for the books, which were in various known places; their positions never changed. On the canterbury were ancient souvenir copies of *The Illustrated London News*, containing pictures of coronations and jubilees and outbreaks of war. In the drawing-room on the shelves below the china ornaments were bound volumes of *Punch*, Joseph Hooker's signed memoirs, John Forster's *Life of Charles Dickens*, without a mention of Ellen Ternan, and a modest selection of the classics. There was also on the bottom shelf a collection of old leather-bound school books with the names of our Avern forbears in brown ink on the fly-leaves. Sometimes there was more than one name in twirls of copperplate, a gazetteer of the world as it was in 1759, when 'Lewis XV' was on the throne of France and New York was listed as 'subject to Great Britain', information made even more mysterious by 's's' which looked like 'f's'. There was a guide book to London dated 1826, containing bewildering information. ' . . . Markets. Those for Hay and Straw are held three times a week in a street called Haymarket.' 'The capital is supplied with 1200 hackney coaches and chariots and with a number of cabriolets and sedan chairs. Three thousand wherries or boats ply on the Thames for hire. Stage coaches for conveyance to and from circumjacent towns and villages abound to a degree nowhere else to be seen.'

A manual on modern etiquette in 'Public and Private', revised and reissued in 1889, was equally illuminating if sometimes no longer valid. 'When in town you must always wear a high hat. . . . It is costly, it is heavy, it is unpicturesque and stiff looking, but nevertheless it has one merit in its favour – that it makes a man look like a gentleman. In the country, however, a high hat looks ridiculous. . . .' ' . . . Man gives precedence to woman in every particular; he does not eat himself till she is served, he is careful to give her the best place at an entertainment, he lets her walk on the inside of the path and opens the door for her when she is leaving the room. Woman was wise in forming society for these small observances not only conduce to her own comfort but are highly beneficial to the character of man, who would without them become rough and selfish.'

'Women's Lib' was yet to come.

Upstairs in the bedroom which came to be 'mine' were other treasures of bygone generations, sad, improving tales of saintly slum-dwellers who died on the last page. The horror of already knowing their fates made re-reading these books a masochistic exercise. *Brave Nelly or Weak Hands and a Willing Heart*. Rivers of tears were shed over dear Nelly's struggles to save her parents from the gin, before she sank into an early grave.

Then there were small bound black volumes of a publi-

34

cation called *The Little Gleaner,* which were already museum pieces in our mother's childhood. In the hand they looked like bibles and strangers were often impressed by our holy choice of reading matter. These were also unbearably sad; even worse, they were alleged to be true, being the last moments of pious children who died young in four-poster beds, spouting texts to the last and illustrated by woodcuts of weeping onlookers in crinolines and stove-pipe hats. My mother told me that when she was a child these books and *The Quiver* were the only reading matter considered suitable for Sundays, but I read them over and over, weekdays and Sundays, absorbed, fascinated and harrowed. There were some books like *The Mill on the Floss,* which were considered unsuitable for my infant mind, but the volumes of *The Little Gleaner* did not come into this category luckily and were my instant choice. In time we came to know them by heart.

Another source of reading was to be found in a tapestry-covered box full of prayer books and bibles and signed leaflets of hymns composed by the Havergal sisters, whom my grandfather had known as a child. They sent these every year instead of Christmas cards. The prayer books were also of varying degrees of age, some of them requiring blessings on the undeserving heads of the early Georges. I was not so spiritually minded that I read this kind of thing from choice but sometimes at the end of two months I was hard-pressed for reading matter. Yet I do not ever remember reading a newspaper. They must have been there, for neat squares of them hung in the lavatory and my grandfather went to sleep in a deckchair on the lawn with newsprint shading his eyes, yet the Great War came and went, the heroes returned and the Depression was upon us before I read a newspaper in my grandmother's house. The time spent there had its own permanence insulated from the world, particularly from London, which was our home. We understood that our father, by the mere fact of marrying our mother and living and working there, put us in a strange exotic environment, not by any means better, merely different, and when we were in our grandparents' house, one which was totally forgotten as we re-read the same old copies of the magazines still there on the top of the music which we all attempted to play on the tinkling piano. Its pleated silk front had been replaced by fretwork over dark red velvet. Although it had belonged to Sir Hubert Parry it was not often tuned and in damp weather two notes were liable to stick, so it will be readily appreciated that my grandmother's family were not outstanding musicians. When we started my father sometimes vanished, for we all had voices and liked to use them, not good voices necessarily, but that did not deter us from giving spirited versions of anything from Handel's 'Largo' to 'The Blue Bells of Scotland'. Our older cousins' renderings of 'A Perfect Day' and 'Somewhere a Voice is Calling' were made even more moving because their husbands were gone to fight in the war, so that even a slight flatness did not prevent us from enjoying a prick of tears on the eyelids. On this piano my mother, my grandmother and my great-grandmother had performed and we now demonstrated how we had or had not progressed in the intervals between our visits. For the Sunday hymns either Lily or my mother played the accompaniments. At our grandmother's house we were not allowed to knit or sew or play cards on this holy day and we gladly filled in the evening singing 'There's a Friend for Little Children' or 'Onward Christian Soldiers' so loudly that the ornaments jumped on the lace runner which covered the top of the piano, the candles rattled in their sockets and only the pained ear of my father could have detected the two notes which did not work.

I regret to admit that I was given to reciting. From nursery rhymes I progressed over the years to 'Paul Revere's Ride' and the 'Ode to a Grecian Urn', which the grown-ups endured with some degree of heroism, for I liked my poems to be dramatic and above all long. Once started I was difficult to stop. I was being given elocution lessons and began to cherish secret dreams of a stage career. When in early teens, being then as tall as I am now – a long drink of water as everyone said when they were not telling me to stand up, sit straight, keep my shoulders back or my tummy in – my kind elocution mistress gently pointed out that to succeed, if you were tall, you had to be exceptionally good or exceptionally beautiful, preferably both. It was clear I was neither of these things and I saw the force of her argument, yet for some reason being the ugly duckling of this handsome family did not depress me unduly, even though no one suggested that I might improve, but I did have a certain amount of faith in prayer. I prayed nightly with great fervour that someone – anyone – would want to marry me, so that I did not have to end my days as a spinster. It did not occur to me that there could be more than one and nobody was more surprised than I when I later found that I had a choice.

5

Have you marked but the fall of the snow,
Before the soil hath smutched it?

Ben Jonson

Owing to their vast breeding propensities it was inevitable that some of our mother's cousins were our own age and we were never short of companions. I freely admit that I was not a good child and I found trying the frequent references to the exemplary behaviour of my mother and Lily and Rose. Once, to a shocked audience I announced that they must have been Awful Prigs, as the only sin which my mother would admit was 'Reading In The Mornings', something my grandmother still considered to be a waste of time, and therefore I committed this crime in the lavatory or up a tree or even while walking down the lane to deliver a message. My mother later confessed to me that she had also done this. The only prank which she and her sisters would recall was so unbelievable that we listened to the description of it over and over again in open-mouthed amazement. Surely, we thought, no one could be so stupid.

Apparently, so we were told, Lily and Rose, led by our mother, had once crept up the stairs and gone to bed *early*, in order to gloat over the search for them when bedtime came. We were relieved to hear that they were not punished for such idiocy. They were merely told that they were all getting far too cheeky. It is fair to assume that they did not lead such unblemished lives as they asserted, but they grew up, so they declared, with few cross words and no raised voices and this I can believe, for our grandparents' house was permeated by a peculiar peace. Even our father, whose temper had a low flash point, seemed to shout at us less when he was there. My mother once told me that during the first year of her married life she had been amazed that although in a large crisis he would remain calm and resourceful, small things could cause voluble irritation, for her own father had never raised his voice other than in laughter.

'Daddy is breathing fire and smoke,' we used to say at home and take evasive action, but, however provoked, our grandfather never appeared to be ruffled. In his blue eyes there was always a sympathetic twinkle.

When I was about eight and Jack four, Joseph came to live across the green. I will not say that he led us astray exactly for I was only too ready to be an accomplice in his crimes. He was the adored child of elderly parents and a row of little graves in the churchyard of the other children, who came between him and his grown-up sister, made him a precious object. Thus he was allowed a freedom which amazed us. Indeed there were moments when I was actually filled with scorn for his white-haired father, who occasionally emerged from his study, and for his gentle little mother. She was the only person I ever saw really wringing her hands, as they say. She often did this, poor woman, clasping and unclasping her fingers as she despairingly called upon her son to come down from the roof, to stop frightening the chickens with his peashooter or blocking the gutters with tennis balls. All this was in vain. Joseph, to our astonished admiration, took absolutely no notice. Indeed, he always seemed to be larger and more powerful than his parents. Whatever happened he was the boss.

He was ten years old at the time.

All the houses round the green had outbuildings, empty stables and coach-houses, for the horses had gone and the cars had not then appeared to take their places. There were barns which were later converted into precious little cottages with carriage lamps and ships' bells and wrought-iron gates but in our time they were our own secret hideaways. We spent days running in and out and up and down in deserted buildings which were untenanted by anything but equine ghosts.

Sherwood House had in bygone days been occupied by Mrs Henry Wood, who wrote the tattered copy of *Mrs Halliburton's Troubles* over which I cried every holiday. For a long time during our childhood the place was empty and we played in the neglected gardens and rolled down the uncut banks and climbed the trees, looked on by the bow windows, which gave us glassy blank stares beneath the curved eyebrows of the wistaria branches. This house now had modern stables but in a shrubby corner was a smaller tumbledown building with a hayloft, where in former more modest days a pony and trap had been kept, and as it was considered unsafe we had been forbidden to go anywhere near it.

When Joseph told us that not only were we going to play in this stable but we were going to climb into and explore the loft above it, we did not demur. I am not altogether blaming him for what happened because I should doubtless have placed bombs in strategic places at his behest.

I was clay in his hands.

The trapdoor which led into the loft was so small it only just fitted us and it was reached by a broken ladder fixed precariously to the wall, which made even Joseph slightly apprehensive. He therefore suggested that we should man-handle Jack through first of all and Jack wanted to stay safely on the ground. He was swiftly overruled. I will not say that we jabbed knives into his fat little calves or lit fires under his chubby bottom, but we forced the loudly protesting child up and through the hole in a manner which only just fell short of torture. Once Jack was installed Joseph gave me a helping hand before he came up himself.

We had scarcely finished exploring, with pleasurable excitement, the dark cavern in which we found ourselves when we heard the church clock across the valley strike one, followed by our grandfather's long low whistle, and we were aware that if we had experienced difficulty in getting up the broken ladder, it was nothing to the difficulty we faced in getting down. In fact Jack flatly refused to attempt the terrifying descent. After fruitless efforts to persuade him, even Joseph realized that we could not throw him through the trapdoor, neither could we leave him there for ever, so we urged him to be brave. When he said he did not want to be brave we mocked him. The cries of various grown-ups calling from all directions only added to our anxiety, so we tried to stiffen his courage by frightening him. He would be eaten by rats, we said, but though he started to cry he would not budge.

It was now clear that we needed assistance and it was decided that Joseph should fetch his father, as being a person likely to help and at the same time not to scold us for disobedience. With daring, Joseph hurled himself down through the space and jumped to the floor. Above, Jack and I waited.

His father, when he appeared below us, blinking up through his glasses, proved his son to be right about the blame but wrong about the help. He was worse than useless. He was too fat to get through the hole and his plaintive appeals to Jack to come to the edge and be lifted down had no effect at all, for the poor child had by this time retired to a corner away from the terrifying abyss and was quietly crying into the hay.

Joseph's father now uttered the only words he ever spoke which roused me, so dreadful were they.

'We must fetch your father,' he said.

Through a gap in the bricks we saw him walk across the green, heard the squeak of the gate and the murmuring of voices. We saw our father's stiff white collar gleaming in the sun as we awaited retribution.

It was at this moment that Joseph vanished. One minute he was below, looking up at me through the trapdoor and the next he was gone and had been replaced by our father's stern face.

'Jack!' he called. 'Come here at once!'

Immediately Jack came out of his corner and appeared at the edge of the chasm and was lifted down. I followed unaided, unwilling to admit that the descent presented any difficulties or indeed that I too was terrified.

I don't recall how our friendship with Joseph came to an end. Perhaps it was after water from the bathroom cascaded down his front stairs like Niagara Falls. I still remember his mother's mild rebukes. 'Joseph, darling!' she said. 'And I did ask you not to . . . ' Jack and I, standing in the hall waiting for our friend to shoot the rapids, at that moment despised her. We also despised his ineffectual father who surveyed the scene in horror but in silence. That is not to say we did not like them both. We did. Indeed we loved them, for they were lovable, long-suffering saints, but, without knowing why, we preferred our own surroundings. There we felt safer. The heady sense of danger was missing; we knew where we were – we knew exactly where we were – and it was reassuring.

One day we were told that our friend had gone to Australia. If he is still alive and undamaged I feel sure he must have made his mark even on the Australians.

We had other holiday friends who were better behaved. There was a family of four, two boys and two girls, on whom we were on more formal visiting terms. They lived at the bottom of the lane and once every summer we were invited there and my grandmother, ever mindful of social obligations, in the course of time asked them back. For these functions we all wore our best clothes, our guests in Eton suits or muslins according to sex. They were so well behaved that it was difficult to entertain them and at tea their silence was so daunting that Lily always started up 'I spy' or 'I love my love with an A'. We all ploughed our way through our love life and the alphabet and two home-made cakes and an iced victoria sponge and tomato sandwiches and brown and white bread and butter and two kinds of jam, besides jellies and sausage rolls. On the days they came it seems in my memory that it always rained and after tea we played 'Beggar My Neighbour' and 'Old Maid'.

In spite of the dullness of the entertainment offered to our guests, they were never anxious to leave. Lily lamented afterwards that they wore their 'sitting breeches' and they would still be there, mouselike and obedient, when my grandfather came home and became restive for his supper. Because of the maturity of the eldest who was twelve, no one came to fetch them. There they lingered as we shuffled and re-dealt the cards with less and less enthusiasm. In the end they had to be scattered forcibly by our desperate grandmother, even her hospitality strained to breaking point.

'Well,' she would ask, gracious but meaningful. 'Have you brought your coats?' This useful saying for removing guests who overstay their welcome is still used by us all to this very day, if not actually aloud, then in our hearts.

6

When the Malvern Hills wear a cap,
Men in the valley beware of that.

Worcestershire proverb

A day at Malvern and a ride to the top of the Beacon on a
donkey was our annual treat. You could also ride on ponies
but ponies were sixpence and a donkey only fourpence; it
need hardly be said that there was never any question about
the animals which were at our disposal. They were always
donkeys. None the less the ride was the high spot of the
holiday. I now deplore that I was never in the least sorry
either for the boy limping behind me goading the poor
animals or for our overworked and often overloaded steeds.

From the window of our grandparents' bedroom, before
the trees grew up to block it, there was a spreading view of
the Malverns and every morning my grandfather would
look out at the hills, ever-changing yet eternal, before
giving a forecast of the weather. He was seldom wrong. If
we could distinguish the paths running clearly like white
threads across the grassy slopes, with the hills distinct against
the sky, then, he explained, the sunshine was not to be
trusted and just an elusive 'Pride of the Morning', which
would soon give way to rain; but should there be a row of
blue bumps we could hope for fine weather. This was the
same wavy outline which we saw from the train and meant
that we were really in Worcestershire and our mother had
come home. It was the signal for us to gather up our clutter
and prepare for our grandfather's welcoming face at Shrub

Hill station. (It was part of the unexplained mysteries of life that there were two stations, neither of them called Worcester.) When we grew up and travelled by car the impact of arrival was never the same, the first view of the hills never so dramatic. Every rise in the ground was compared with the Worcestershire Beacon, everything was measured against it from the Wrekin to Mont Blanc.

'It's just like Malvern, only higher,' my mother told me when she brought me hopefully, with advanced tuberculosis, to Davos, and in a way she was right for all hill resorts have an affinity, a feeling of hope that life goes on and up.

To reach Malvern from Lower Wick, in the days before cars or an adequate bus service, meant a train journey on a now defunct line. First we walked to Henwick station, a mile along the Malvern Road, always arriving, owing to our grandmother's frantic urgings, much too early. She presumably enjoyed a day of peace without us. She was there when we returned, ready to hear of our incredible adventures.

The wait was enlivened by the initial excitements of buying tickets, watching the man in the box operate the signals and actually being encouraged to walk across the forbidden rails at the level crossing to reach the other platform, until at last we were all in the train travelling through the hopyards and orchards towards the hills. Once a mistake was made and we alighted too soon at Malvern Link, giving ourselves a long hot walk into the town. Even the proper station, grandly labelled 'Great Malvern' and somehow more important than other places by being 'Great', was still a good way from St Anne's Well, where our real climb would start. We might have been contemplating an ascent of the Matterhorn. Although we never chose a wet day we took the wise precaution of being prepared for all emergencies and were always burdened with mackintoshes and umbrellas. In addition we carried lavish provisions.

We all wore our best clothes and, of course, hats, Jack in his new panama, which he was just learning to doff when he met a lady and remove on the doorstep of any house. Only with difficulty was he persuaded to take it

45

off in church. He did not consider that church was a house and he was only parted from it there after an audible struggle, which filled me, so much older and wiser, with the deepest shame. He was inevitably vanquished, for a battle of this nature was not a thing which even Jack was likely to win.

At St Anne's Well the grown-ups rested, puffing slightly and mopping their brows, all except our grandfather who, to the end of his days, sprang up and down his native hills with the agility of a mountain goat. The first thing to be done here was to give the blind man a penny. He sat playing a little harmonium and he smiled when he heard the chink of our donation and looked at us with filmed, unseeing eyes, which I found alarming. No one explained to us the sadness of the poor man sitting there playing the cheerful tunes of the day to a world he could not see. We had to give him our penny with our own hands and we did so, but with a terror so hard to describe that we did not try. Only when we were grown up did we compare notes about it. After this ordeal we were obliged, for the supposed good of our health, to 'Drink the Waters', and this we did with equal unthinking obedience from an iron cup of doubtful hygiene attached to the well by a chain. Our stoicism was rewarded by an apple from our grandfather's pocket (which was always made shapeless by a bottomless pit of apples) and a penny bar of Peter's chocolate from the slot machine, which was divided between us.

With the knowing eyes of horse copers we then embarked on the ceremony of choosing our donkeys. Camp Three was forsaken and, prodded by the sticks of our donkey boys, our steeds began the slow ascent to the summit, followed by our perspiring elders on foot and burdened with the picnic baskets. At the top we did not actually raise the Union Jack but the atmosphere was a mixture of triumph coupled with sadness at having to part with our donkeys, as the boys were paid off and, forsaking the paths, galloped down through the bracken with an abandon which filled us with envy. The grown-ups having toiled behind us like an army of Sherpas, would then hopefully look for a picnic spot out of the wind. If this came from the west we huddled under the rocks on the opposite side and looked at Worcestershire. If from the east, then Herefordshire lay at our feet, running away into the far mountains of Wales, mysteriously blue and not black as their name suggested. There was an indicator on the top which told us where to find the Wrekin, the North Hill and the British Camp. The Bristol Channel, the Quantocks and Snowdon we took on trust. They were alleged to be discernible on the hazy horizon, and I believed this because in those days I believed everything I was told. Honesty compels me to say that I never distinguished them any more than now, living in the Quantock area have I ever seen the Malverns, which are supposed to be visible in the misty distance. Looking south-eastward from the Beacon was different, for we could pick out houses and churches which we knew and we could see the Severn snaking its way to the cathedral, its tributary, the Teme, watering the land of our relations and the fields we knew so well. We could, in fact, almost trace our route right back to our grandparents' house, as we lay amongst the harebells and heather, chewing grass stalks and scanning the checkerboard below, which stretched away and away into the end of things until it must reach our exiled home in London. The top of the Worcestershire Beacon was an education in itself. Somehow from our father or our grandfather we came to know that Jenny Lind was called the Swedish Nightingale and the house which was once hers lay just below us in the trees; that our grandfather's friend, Edward Elgar, who wrote 'Land of Hope and Glory', lived on the other side of the hill; that the Jubilee Drive had been made because a queen called Victoria had lived to be very old; that monks had built the Abbey; that the Wrekin was in Shropshire; that Piers Plowman had a vision here, and long, long ago the Romans and Ancient Britons had fought battles here with sling shots just like our own forbidden catapults. It all combined into a garbled story which we effortlessly absorbed. The skin of a marauding Dane which had been nailed to the cathedral door was mixed up with King John's tomb inside

47

and the Victorian marble figure of Bishop Philpott, who was our grandmother's cousin. Some were Good. Some were Bad. No reasons were given. Everything was mysteriously simplified and the marshes, where the Welsh had been driven, were not marshes at all but 'marches', which meant borders.

Thus, in the recesses of consciousness, was the Marchshire of my novels born. It has also something of a second love, the Kentish Weald, where I lived for a good deal of my married life. In some ways Worcestershire and Kent resemble each other, especially in the cultivation of hops and fruit. In Kent they call kilns 'oasts' and hopyards are 'hopfields', but the scent of the hop in September and the magic of the orchards in spring are common to each, so that in an imaginary county they easily merge. When I write about Marchshire I can enjoy them both all over again.

The downward path, like all downward paths, was much easier than the upward struggle and at the bottom we were dusted and tidied up and given pennies to go to the lavatory, a small building discreetly hidden in the bushes. Jack, whose bladder required constant attention at embarrassing moments, had already been taken off behind the rocks for frequent calls of nature. The process for him was unfairly simple, but I was perforce made capable of more self-control. Thus relieved at last, hats straightened, socks adjusted, our faces were roughly cleaned in a manner we both found revolting even if it was our own spit. It was a method we deplored but we were on our way to have tea at a restaurant and we realized that for such grandeur some suffering was inevitable.

The improbably yellow cake, thick bread and butter and red jam, which did not taste or look at all like the jam made by our grandmother, were fallen upon by us as if they were ambrosia and we had not eaten for weeks. Our elders restored themselves with strong tea before we finally turned our backs on the hills. Everything after the culminating glory at the café was an anti-climax, or perhaps we were all just tired. Perhaps our over-corseted aunts were uncomfortable, perhaps the stiff, white collars of our grandfather and father had begun to chafe. I seem to recall that this was the point when we began to be on the receiving end of reproof. Now was the time when it could rain, and once a terrific storm of frightening proportions made us run all the way to the station without even being scolded for enjoying the puddles. On a memorable occasion the rain set in early; our picnic was perforce abandoned and we all actually lunched at an hotel. For years the word 'hotel' meant for me the old Beauchamp. It became part Ritz, part Savoy, something about which to brag when we returned to school, for, alas! there our long happy holiday at our grandparents' house was considered by our London friends to be totally inferior to their fortnight with bucket and spade at Hastings or Bognor. I was eleven before I saw the sea. That other children could be part of the landscape was an affront as well as a surprise after the loneliness and limitless distance of the hills, and the sea appeared to be confined by an edge on which a small ship was perched, as if it were nothing more than an enlarged version of our grandfather's pond. I remember looking at the grey waves from the beach at Lowestoft and being woefully disappointed, for I had pictured it immeasurably bluer and bigger and that I should have it entirely to myself.

Later explorations by car; foreign travel; ships, aeroplanes, that first glimpse of the Alps, the Carpathians; none of this would ever quite reach the pinnacle of bliss when our donkeys took us to the top of the Worcestershire Beacon. After all it was over thirteen hundred feet high and that was very nearly a mountain.

7

Birds flow under the heavens
And seas over their bed
And the endless sea of history
Flows over the dead.

Frederick Prokosch

My grandfather was a regular attender at Powick church
and Lily sang in the choir. Generations of us were married,
christened and buried there and so of course, when we
went to stay at Lower Wick, every Sunday morning we
hopped along at my grandfather's side. In dry weather we
went the 'short' way, through the hopyard over the 'new'
bridge across the water meadows, up the steep steps made
from the beams taken out of the church when it was restored, through the kissing gate which leads to the churchyard, past the sad little mound marked by a dwarf tree,
which was the grave of Anne Elizabeth, our mother's baby
sister, and on into the huge church, where the devout few
were sparsely scattered.

My religion, such as it was, could truly be described as
an accident of birth. Had my parents taken me to a chapel
or a Quaker meeting I should doubtless have gone with
them, unquestioning and unprotesting. They could have
made a Mormon of me, led me to a mosque or a Buddhist
temple. They could have indoctrinated my virgin mind
with the thoughts of Karl Marx or they could have taught me
how to disrupt society. That the first act of worship which I
remember happened to be in Powick church was merely
chance. But I am grateful that it was so; grateful for the
interminable prayers in a language familiar yet incompre-

hensible, for sermons and readings from the Bible far beyond my understanding, for hymns I could sing even before I could read. I am grateful for being brainwashed by beautiful words, for long spaces of time when, though I was forced to sit still, I could let my mind wander – thinking time when I could watch the butterfly asleep in the corner gradually stir and come to life, when I might wonder who the people were whose memorial tablets decorated the walls, and listen to the old man across the aisle sprinkling his aitches in a manner which I found fascinating, although I had been told it must on no account be imitated. 'Pra–h'a–h'aise to the 'oliest h'in the 'e–e–ight' sounded sweetly in my ears.

I could also ponder on what there might be for dinner which, on Sundays, was on an even vaster scale than week-days.

It was an interval for one's own imaginings until one put a hot penny into the bag which Grandpa carried round, and sang the last hymn with joyous thankfulness that it was all over. Soon we would be out in the sunshine, being shown the holes in the wall made by the wicked Cromwell's bullets. Lily, holding on to her best hat, her feet barely touching the ground, would flash past us like the Red Queen, in order to ensure that the Sunday joint was ready to pop into our ravenous mouths after our more leisurely walk home. It was over a mile but we thought nothing of that; from an early age we were accustomed to walk enormous distances, for there was seldom any other method of getting about.

Our grandmother never came with us to church. It was vaguely supposed to be something to do with her legs, combined with the new vicar's innovations in the matter of vestments and intoned prayers. She did not hold with these goings-on but she still welcomed the parson with seed cake and the best Worcester tea-service. All the china was from the Royal Worcester Porcelain works as a matter of course, some of it old and beautiful but despised and used for lowly purposes, such as holding eggs or dripping. When the parson came the set with the pink scrolls came out. It was un-ashamedly hideous but it was the best. I have it now, all twelve cups and saucers and plates, complete with milk jug and a huge slop basin, for the days when the cups had to be warmed with hot water, and two bread-and-butter plates. There is only one crack amongst them, for they were always carefully washed by my grandmother's own hands. Tastes have changed so that now I think these are beautiful as well. This tea-service was part of the Sunday scenery, a day totally different from other days, set apart as a birthday might be or Christmas. Like the pink tea-service, going to church was also part of the Sunday ritual. Religion was never discussed though it was understood in a vague way that whereas good people went to church, some people who were also good did not, for my grandmother was good, there could be no question about that. I also accepted the fact that whereas she might stay at home there was never any question that we might do the same. A habit thus formed, as I later learned, had little to do with religion, or faith or lack of it. It merely left us with a feeling we could not defend that Sunday without church was somehow wrong in itself. Although I am incapable of giving a rational explanation for this statement I am thankful for the peace of dull sermons and badly sung psalms, uncertain organists, beautiful arches and altar flowers, low churches and high churches, cathedral choirs, the English churches in Dresden, Bucharest, Venice, or small groups of exiles, perhaps only half a dozen people, gathered in a school or hall, solaced in a foreign land by the known words of the liturgy.

While freely admitting that church-going can be no more than a habit, I have found in times of stress that it has given comfort and in times of happiness it has brought its own brand of peace. It is something on which I can lean in thankfulness for my upbringing.

On Sunday afternoons we all slept. We were given a chocolate each – a great treat – and we all sank into our feather beds with improving books, knowing no more until the discreet chink of the teacups being brought from the huge pantry, across the tiled kitchen up the steps into the dining-room, roused us and we rose from our slumbers like drowsy bees. Even more visitors came on Sundays, for Lower Wick was then a pleasant country walk from Worcester or from Bransford, or a drive of just the right length for the horse from farther afield, Leigh, Guarlford and Madresfield. The family and all its ramifications of friends and cousins, both first, second and far removed, came uninvited and un-announced, greeted with whoops of acclaim by us children, for not only did they play Croquet with us or Statues or Granny's Steps, or push us on the swing which hung from the cedar tree, but they were often the bearers of sweets, something which in our childhood was a luxury.

Knowing that her own small 'managed' resources might well be needed to bolster their extravagances, there were some of the spendthrifts of her in-laws whom my grand-mother greeted with reserve. It was impossible for her ex-pression to be other than mild, but there were occasions when it could become blank.

Our father called it her 'Can't Be False Look'.

Everyone went away laden with flowers and fruits of the season, after polite and grateful cries of surprise and protest, but there was one in-law who took her plunder for granted and always came armed with an empty basket. On one never-to-be-forgotten day my grandmother's face became more than blank; it became stubborn. The basket was not filled. Aunt Fanny followed her hopefully round the garden and at last at the gate she was driven to despair.

'I've brought my basket,' she said, with tragic emphasis.

Of course, it was filled, but this catch-phrase became part of that private language which belongs to every family. Descendants of our grandparents, now growing up in the Permissive Society, have been known to bleat, 'I've brought my basket' when they laugh off an obvious scrounge with Aunt Fanny's plaintive words. I can picture them taking trips to the moon armed with their baskets, when Aunt Fanny is mere hearsay, a dim figure in the background of long-destroyed wedding groups in a hat like a frying pan, but immortalized by a chance sentence.

On Sundays we were allowed to stay up a little later. Were the summers really better or were we more hardy? We all sat under the cedar tree until it was nearly dark and the bats began to swoop across the lawn and the midges to bite us in the few places exposed to their ravages. At a certain point during the evening my grandmother would send me upstairs to fetch the little white shawl she wore round her shoulders and the men would blow smoke rings to discourage the midges. No women smoked. They were all still there when we were sent, burning with the injustice of it, to bed, after being allowed 'a little longer' by my grandmother. For a while we would keep quite quiet, lurking behind a chair in the hope that we might be forgotten and then a nod from our grandfather or my father and we knew there was no appeal. I was enraged that they should go on enjoying themselves without us. If they had all come into the house I could have borne it. Yet I always fell asleep quickly, watching the moths blunder towards the candle, to an obbligato of chatter and laughter and the occasional hoot of an owl, and knew no more until the morning noises started, the cock crowing across the hopyard, the sound of the pump, the tramp of the farm labourers walking down the lane, the postman's bicycle bell, the smell of frying home-cured bacon and the blissful prospect of Another Day.

Now I can only wonder at my own callousness, for this sensation of utter happiness, which is an abiding memory of the old house, enveloped the bloodstained years of the First World War, the years which started when I was seven and ended when I was eleven. In retrospect they are telescoped into a flash of pictures flickering quickly over a screen, like an old newsreel. They began with my father, who was already dependent on foreign trade, saying that he 'must put up the shutters' and this was in itself mysterious because we had no shutters. It ended with an open-air service and fireworks and flags and being sent home from school, because at last it was all over. In between there were words like Gallipoli and Mons, Verdun and the Somme, a Zeppelin which was a ball of fire in the distance; the uncles and cousins who came in uniform to say 'good-bye', sometimes for the last time, and the soldiers in blue at the hospital where Lily was a V.A.D. Then there were the German prisoners working in the fields, whose bovine faces filled us with such terror. Could it be really true that they ate babies?

I remember my father being ill for a long time; I remember scarcities, the furry taste of the broad-bean pods which we were given to eat at school when food grew short. Jack, being younger, remembers only the Zeppelin but he also has a searing memory that in an access of helpfulness, when our father was ill, I tried to make the tea and in doing so poured a kettle of boiling water on to my brother's back and nearly scalded him to death. Poor boy! It is amazing he survived, but I meant well. I still do.

The war I heard about while I was staying with my grandparents was the one which was fought nearly three hundred years earlier, between the King's men and the wicked Cromwell. Our grandparents' house had stood on a little rise outside Worcester since before the Civil War. The front had been built on in the days of Queen Anne and later two Victorian bays were added to this, but the kitchens and larder were much older and were marked on the old maps as 'The Cottages in the Fields'. Here Prince Rupert was said to have made his last stand and I saw him in my mind brandishing a flag from the roof of the scullery.

In the surrounding meadows and gardens the bloody battles of the seventeenth century had been fought and it was these, rather than the present fighting, which my grandfather described when he found a skull in the begonia bed, or showed me bullet marks on walls. As we leaned over the old bridge with the embrasures to let people stand with safety when the coaches went by, we were told how it ran red with blood. The dip in the Ham Field was where the soldiers who fought for the King lay buried. There was never any question as to whose side we supported. Worcester was not called The Faithful City for nothing and no one had a good word to say for a man like Cromwell, who could stable horses in the cathedral. When my father, who always saw both sides and who was from enemy territory anyway, occasionally put forward an argument on Cromwell's behalf he was instantly shot down for the stranger he was, the man who had come from another land, the eastern counties, to take a good Worcestershire girl to London and make an exile of her. I was grown up before it occurred to me that the romantic Charles might have brought some of his troubles upon himself, for we were King's Men, no doubt about it. Cromwell was a villain and the fact that his nephew was once engaged to be married to one of our forbears was something of which we were not proud. The story was only admitted because the young man was lost at sea before the ceremony could be performed and she had thus married someone else and saved us from having been contaminated by the blood of a Roundhead. There is a miniature of her, sad-faced, resigned, loved by someone with the hated name of Cromwell.

This was the war which seemed nearer to me in the middle of England in 1916 than all the fighting in France, though there was a war wedding with the bridegroom handsome in uniform, and I was an excited bridesmaid; there was my grandfather poring over things called casualty lists; there were cousins who never came back, and then there was the Victory Parade in 1919, which I watched from the window of the bank manager's house in Foregate, together with the bank manager's children and grandchildren. And there was Lily at the head of the procession in her V.A.D. uniform, purposeful, stern and ready to cope with the peace as she had coped with everything else, and even then perhaps aware that she would never marry, now that so many of the men of her generation were gone.

All three of the girls were pretty. My mother had sparkle as well as good looks; Rose was a delicious blue-eyed blonde. My father always called her Rosebud; she had a skin which blushed easily and a gurgling laugh. Lily, with her straight gaze and serious eyes, had not the same charm as her sisters, but the family doctor, looking at her bone structure, assured her that she would make the best-looking old woman. And he was right.

It was during the First World War that I first saw my own words in print, in *Home Chat* in fact, no more but then no less. Mrs Bruin and Tiger Tim inaugurated a competition for an essay on how a child could help in the war effort and for my own contribution I received a War Savings Certificate for the enormous sum of fifteen shillings. What wise suggestions I made are no longer remembered, even by me, but I would point out that we did win the war, or so we were led to believe.

It was not until 1949, more than thirty years later, when my husband and I visited a cemetery outside Arras, that some understanding of that obliteration of youth came to me. By then our own generation had made further sacrifices in six and a half years of a later war, but we were looking for the grave of his nineteen-year-old brother killed in 1916, after only a few weeks at the front. There they lay, eighteen-nineteen-, twenty-year-olds, thousands and thousands of them, marked by regular little stones sticking up like teeth from the blood-soaked soil of France. Time had ripened the carefully tended trees and shrubs which had been planted to soften the starkness of the scene, so that it produced its own special tranquillity but it was not until I saw Faubourg d'Amiens, with its wave upon wave of the familiar midland names of the same regiment in which my husband and his brothers had also served, that the full horror of that other earlier war to end wars really penetrated.

Golden Pavements

8

When my mother accepted my father's offer of marriage it was generally considered that she threw herself away, being pursued as she was at the time by others who were better looking and better off. When, long afterwards, I asked her what had attracted her so that she had made this apparently reckless choice, she thought for a moment and then she said: 'He was much more intelligent than the rest. He was always wanting to know; he was always learning; he made everything interesting,' and then she added: 'and he loved me.'

'But the others must have loved you.'

'Yes, but he loved me more. And he was – somehow – different.'

He was indeed. To start with he came from the foreign territory of the eastern counties where men had always been ambitious and tough and on the side of the hated Cromwell. He was tall and thin and pale; as he grew older he acquired an air of clumsy distinction but he was never as good-looking as the family into which he married. Neither could he boast as they did, of alleged ancestors, for apparently, beyond a great-grandfather who was a signwriter, he knew nothing about them and cared less.

This unknown signwriter imparted to the eventual fruit of his loins an unusual strain of craftsmen and artists. In the course of time it produced painters, architects, inventors, editors, researchers and scholars. It also produced my father. The eldest of seven, he was cleverer than the others, but the only one who could not draw or paint with some degree of skill. His father was a competent artist and the friend of artists, with a remarkable gift for restoring pictures, and his children grew up knowing more about music and painting than was common in the circles of their childhood. As he was really a builder his devotion to his hobbies was possibly the reason that he was not an outstanding financial success, although his hand can be seen in the restoration of many churches in the midlands. His brother and nephew were architects and he should certainly, as a builder in the days of much admittedly horrible development, have been able to make more than just an adequate living, but his artistic qualities did not equip him for this. When a realistic price for his work was suggested he would protest: 'But that would be robbery.' It was his wife who had her eye on more material things. Yet she had rigid standards which prevented her from allowing him to sell a house he owned to a brewery for conversion into a public house, even though a heavy loss was thereby incurred. In many ways this background was similar to The Five Towns of Arnold Bennett. There was the same provincial integrity, the same stifling convention, the same yearning for the stars.

My father and his brothers and sisters were sent to the best schools then available. His mother saw to that. In my father's case it was the Kettering Grammar School, nowadays enjoying an outstanding reputation, but then housed in old, inadequate buildings where, despite or maybe because of various chastisements, he became a good Latin scholar, and carried off many prizes. That he became a chemist was an accident. The local pharmacy owed my grandfather money and offered to take the boy as an apprentice in settlement of the debt. He had wanted to be a doctor, but this being impossible due to lack of funds, after an abortive attempt at journalism, he settled for becoming a pharmacist, and he was a good one, passing his examinations in record time with self-denial and black coffee, and coming out amongst the best in all England. He did not intend to remain behind a counter, though he was always proud of the fact that he was one of the first members of the Pharmaceutical Society and had trained in the bad old days the hard way. In his time chemists diagnosed and prescribed for those who could not afford doctors and for this part of his work my father had an uncanny talent which he never lost. When misfortune hit him, and it often did for his working life embraced two world wars and a slump, he would say: 'I can always go back to being a chemist.' (In his old age he found himself having to wash up, a rite he performed wearing a hat – for the kitchen was draughty – and smoking a cigar, and he would murmur, with a kind of morose satisfaction, 'I began by washing bottles and I could end washing bottles.')

After the initial shock of the impact of this stranger my mother's father welcomed his prospective son-in-law and they became firm friends. A male in that female-ridden household was a happy addition and as keen a botanist as my father was even more welcome. (Somehow, between them, these two men painlessly imparted so much botanical knowledge that, from the age of eleven until I matriculated, I scarcely bothered to listen to the botany mistress.) They would go off together in a conspiratorial manner and return rather cheerful from the Hopmarket. They shared the same dry humour but my father could sometimes be biting as well as amusing and my grandmother was always a little nervous of him. She respected his advice, which she often sought but less often took, for it was Lily who always thought she knew better and in that house, from her early girlhood, Lily was the boss. For my father's part he loved them all dearly and he basked in the easy warmth which my mother's family effortlessly generated.

He was an impatient man. He had no tact and made no effort to charm. Perhaps his undeviating honesty was the reason for this. For him the ordinary course of day to day life was either right or wrong; there could be no middle way, no grey areas. He was ambitious. He wanted to show all those who had thought my mother could have done better

63

for herself that they were wrong, and this, in time, he was able to do.

When he married he had escaped from the tyranny of dispensing and had his first foot on the ladder, working for Burroughs Wellcome, but he was impatient of slow progress, though he afterwards learnt he was a man already noticed for higher things. Pressed on by ambition and youthful lack of judgment he left and joined a smaller firm, unaware that it was in financial difficulties. He soon had cause to regret his lack of foresight when it went into liquidation and he found himself suddenly out of a job with a wife and child and another on the way. He always maintained that this whole episode was a challenging and salutary experience; one which he did not repeat, though it left him with a permanent sympathy for the misfortunes of others.

He was the kind of man whose hard-working tenacity would have made an eventual success of anything which he undertook, but he would never have made a million. He was too honest and too generous, and although he could be hard he could not be ruthless.

'I wanted her to have everything,' he said to me when my mother died, 'and I did not want either you or Jack to struggle as I had to.'

To this end he drove himself, working long hours with few holidays, spending more than he could afford on our education, as he overcame setbacks and pressed on and up the ladder. His ambitions were all for us and his standards were so high that they were necessarily out of reach.

It was from his mother that my father inherited his ambition, for this was the driving force which carried her, a woman who did not really want children, through seven births and numerous miscarriages. She was small, plain, but distinguished looking and by the time I remember her she was already crippled with rheumatism. This affliction and her eventual sufferings from cancer of the throat she bore with the fortitude she expected from others, for there seemed to be little softness in her, or if there was she hid it. When we spent a few days there at dutiful intervals we knew we had to be on our best behaviour and, aware of a certain tension on the part of our mother, we really did try. The house had an arid perfection which was entirely missing from my mother's home. It had electric light when this was still something of a miracle, a bathroom with a hot-water system which actually worked, and a choice of lavatories. My two youngest aunts, Alice and Ella, were in their early teens when I was born and they were both very good to me, fashioning for me fascinating things and encouraging me to make dolls' clothes and calendars for myself. I made only moderate progress but they were proud of being such young aunts, though they never seemed any younger, or even as young as, the laughing Rose and Lily and all that army of Worcestershire relations, for there was a seriousness about them, while they lived in their parents' house. There even my own parents seemed different.

When my mother was taken to meet her future in-laws before she married, Alice and Ella were still children and were brought down to meet her. Their white faces were emphasized by white nightdresses, for all the family had an unearthly pallor. It did not stop them from living to great ages but it gave them all the appearance of having just emerged from a cellar. (I suffered also from this until I was later bold enough to put matters right behind locked doors with illicit rouge.)

They told me afterwards that they thought my mother at nineteen was the most wonderful thing they had ever seen.

'We loved her from the moment we saw her,' said Alice, 'and we've always loved her.'

My mother was touched by their fragile, pathetic appearance and for this reason she loved them also.

These two children grew up to be talented women of character. When they were young they often came to stay and it was then that I grew close to them. For a long time I was the only grand-daughter and in so far as any member of my father's family was capable of uncritical affection, Alice and Ella made much of me and I learnt a great deal from them. There was an older sister, another Lily, who was my godmother, and she was also good to me. Indeed all my aunts, on both sides of the family, have always shown me kindness beyond my deserts, but my father's family, being themselves so gifted, seemed harder to please.

My mother's views on our clothes were considered to be advanced but whereas in her own family circle nothing was said of her outlandish London ways, at Kettering it was made clear that socks on a great girl of nine constituted an affront to decency. I clearly remember while we were staying there being taken with haste to a shop to be equipped with my first black stockings. The 'short' sleeves of my dresses, although they covered my bony elbows and today would be described as 'three-quarters', were considered not only a vulgar display but likely to lead to pneumonia. To keep us out of mischief our mother took us for long walks in the new park, where the swings and slides had been invented, made and given by a relation of my father's. It was a forerunner of many such playgrounds and here we worked off some of our exuberance and were given buns so that our indelicate appetites did not arouse adverse comment.

Why should my memories of this house be so chilly? Perhaps because I was instantly bitten by my bachelor uncle's dog and the gold coin, which was always given to us by this grandmother when we left, was peculiarly useless because it could not be spent like less exotic contributions. There was also an alarming table in the drawing-room which my father's father had painted so that it looked exactly like marble. He was supposed to be one of the only two men in England who could do this and nothing was ever allowed to be put upon it. After once being scolded for making the mistake of thinking that a table was for just this purpose, I became frightened of it and remained uncomforted by my mother's secret whisperings that it was hideous.

He was a kind but inaccessible grandparent, painting or restoring his pictures in his workshop, or tending his geraniums in the greenhouse, a withdrawal due not so much to unsociability as to the disapproval of his wife for his pipe. Now I regret that I was not nearer to this remarkable man, so that I could have profited from his deep knowledge of pictures and architecture. All I remember are dark Landseer-like paintings of animals and the almost invisible little faces (until one looked closely) which he fashioned from the knots in the woodwork of the wardrobe in my young aunts' bedroom. To them he must have been a delightful and understanding parent but he was dead before I could appreciate him or the charming portraits of them which he painted. His dry humour I only knew in my own father.

My father's grandmother was still alive – a good boasting point, for none of our friends possessed such a rarity as a great-grandmother. Moreover she was born in the year of Waterloo and was thus nearly a hundred. I remember being taken to see her and on suddenly being confronted with a bony face in a white nightcap peering at me over the sheets, I confused her with the wolf impersonating Red Riding Hood's grandmother and was overcome by terror. After I had been taken screaming from the room they said I had blotted my copybook. In this exercise book, where I was learning to write, by laboriously copying pious maxims after progress from pot-hooks, only pencil was allowed, so there could be no question of blotting anything, and the accusation remained all the more mystifying as I had not even taken it with me.

The best part of our stay with our father's parents was the journey there and back across the impenetrable midlands, a campaign complicated by three changes, sandwiches on the train and the excitement of a taxi at both ends. Although it was only sixty miles it would have been simpler to have gone back to London and out again via Paddington and St Pancras, but this would have cost more and was therefore not even considered, despite the fact that the cross-country journey took nearly all day. We were enthusiastic travellers; my father, however, seldom came with us. Wisely armed with good excuses he set off later and departed earlier, leaving my mother to charm the porters and stop us from driving our fellow passengers demented.

She was born with an itching foot. A map, a railway timetable, a picture of a foreign country was enough to start her dreams. How often did we not listen to our parents' plans for going across Canada or up the Amazon and the sad fact that by the time they had both the leisure and the money to achieve this, they would be too old for such adventures, was hidden in the merciful mists of the future. Yet to the end of her days my mother could view the prospect of a journey, however small, as an adventure. Anywhere which was new, an unknown village, a different route, she regarded as exploration and she would set off, even in old age, on a day out as if it were a voyage of discovery. Everything with her became as A. A. Milne would have said 'an expotition'. She missed nothing and she allowed us to miss nothing. From the top deck of a London bus we were made to notice the name of every street and side street and all the stations of the hated Underground, undeterred by the disadvantage that both of us were often travel-sick. We grew up to recognize landmarks, to be familiar with the routes and numbers of the buses, to know which railway ran into which terminus and the byways of the City when we were taken to our father's office; the curves of the Thames and the names of the bridges which crossed it. The Thames, we were told, was England's most important river, but we were not allowed to forget that our mother's own Severn was longer.

She taught us the mechanics of travelling. Jack, she decreed, although the youngest, must always be in charge of us, because he was A MAN. So Jack, scarcely tall enough to see the booking clerk, had to buy the tickets and generally look after us. She did not actually make him lift suitcases as big as himself on to the luggage racks, but it was his duty to count the pieces and see that we alighted at the right station. He had to supervise the trunk which if not sent 'in advance' had to go into the luggage van. He must see that it was labelled correctly and he must watch its actual transfer into the van. It was just no good, he was told, relying on the porter to do this. A distrustful habit thus inculcated persisted into late middle age. The porter, Jack learnt, had to be thanked, tipped and generally treated with courtesy; with our attractive mother around there was never any shortage of assistance.

The first time she went to Paris she had a day alone there before meeting me off my train from Davos. I was by then grown up. There she stood on the platform, beaming and waving with a particularly villainous-looking, unshaven Frenchman by her side.

'Be nice to him,' she whispered. 'He has looked after me all day.'

I discovered he was a taxi-driver who spoke English and as her knowledge of French was minimal and her pronunciation appalling, she had asked him to give her a potted tour of Paris, so that she could see as much as possible before I arrived in the evening.

'He has been wonderful,' she said, opening her bag and telling him to help himself to what she owed him.

'I don't understand the money,' she explained, 'so this is how we manage,' and she smiled that disarming innocent smile of hers.

It would be a villain indeed who could cheat her and she seldom was cheated, but dishonesty was the one thing which made her angry. (I remember her buying some peaches for me when I was ill and had a fancy for such a luxury. It turned out that she had been sold a bad one and she could hardly believe in such iniquity.)

After an almost tearful farewell from the taxi-driver on the hotel steps, I was greeted in the bedroom by a bewildered chambermaid. She gazed at me in some astonishment and then began to laugh. In a flood of French she explained that when my mother had told her to make up the second bed, she had asked if it was for her husband.

'Non! Non!' my mother had said, but her French being insufficient to explain that it was for her daughter, who was arriving from Switzerland, the woman had concluded that the room was being prepared for her lover. When I told this to my mother she could scarcely credit such a supposition and made shocked noises.

'Really! The French . . . '

Yet I suspect she was a little flattered.

'Perhaps we had better not tell your father,' she said.

Alas! when she was young she had little opportunity of going far. A trip to Germany, holidays in France, a visit to Switzerland was all she ever achieved, for although my father was perpetually coming home and announcing that the next day he had to go to Paris, to Cologne, to Prague, to Vienna, when we were children she never thought of accompanying him, or if she thought of it she kept it to herself. For the whole of our childhood she was simply THERE and anything else was unthinkable. We would rush home from school or from visits to friends and relations, clatter up the stairs and there she would be in the bow window of her bedroom, sewing. It faced south and I am not saying the sun always shone on her, but that is how it seems in restrospect, as she put down her needle and listened to all we had to tell her.

9

My crown is in my heart, not on my head,
Not decked with diamonds and Indian stones,
Not to be seen. My crown is called content.

Shakespeare

All writers of books such as this are prone to dwell on the beauty of their mothers. A tense female in an unbecoming hair-do, gazing with apprehension at the camera, illustrates the description of a superlatively beautiful goddess, scented and in evening dress, bending over their cots. This is an alleged first memory. Perhaps because our mother so seldom wore an evening dress I have no such recollection, but as my father fell in love with her at first sight and pursued her with characteristic determination I am prepared to cede that she must have been beautiful. She was, I am told, tall with regular features and in her brown hair there was a chestnut gleam. She had a good figure and an air of elegance, for she dressed simply but with taste, having pitifully few clothes in our childhood days. However, they were always as good as she could afford so that she had a well-dressed air. 'The poorer you are, the fewer clothes you have, the better they must be,' was one of her maxims with which my father agreed. His few suits were from a good tailor and his shoes were hand-made. I was happy to point them out at school functions as my parents. They made an attractive pair, for my father, despite his stoop, was even taller than his wife, his face, though not in the least handsome, was both sensitive and intelligent and I was aware of being proud of them. There was never the slightest chance of their letting us down, as other parents sometimes did, by peculiar behaviour or funny hats, but if people looked at my mother, and they did (for although I do not remember her actual looks, I recall that heads turned when she appeared) she was instantly embarrassed at this attention and thought it must be due to a smut on her nose or a descending petticoat.

As a girl, in a hat and a long dress, which she held up in one hand, she had played tennis well with an old-fashioned racket shaped like the letter P and used by us for french cricket. When we grew older she played with us, winning not with better play but with her calm persistence and patient unfailing returns. She played both tennis and badminton until she was over fifty, something which in those days was unusual, and she remained a dedicated walker, for she never learned to drive a car. It was when she could no longer do these things that she gradually began to gain weight, but she had long legs and held herself well, so that somehow it suited her and merely added to her air of good-tempered benevolence. She was still graceful and upright, even when she was handicapped by arthritis, but she was never strong-minded enough to do anything about her weight problem, and when she died her desk was found to be full of slimming diets and luscious defeating recipes. To the end her extra pounds only added to her air of loving kindness.

This is what I remember.

Beauty apart, our mother had the supreme quality of being easy to live with for she had inherited her father's tolerance. Once when I asked her why she was so good-tempered she answered, 'I just don't feel angry,' sounding almost apologetic, as if acknowledging a fault. She always maintained that she was shy, but as she found no difficulty in establishing instant contact with everybody and anybody I do not think this is quite true. Her charm came largely from the fact that she thought others might be nervous too, and in striving to set them at their ease she forgot herself. Her alleged shyness was merely diffidence and it often established immediate contact, because she felt the person to whom she was talking had more important things to say than she had, so she became a receptive listener as well as a lively talker – an unusual combination. From the smallest outing she came back with tales of adventures. She had seen this, she had done the other and she had met Mrs Somebody Else. The Lord Mayor's banquet yielded no more excitements than a visit to the shops, and her weekly letters to us after we left home were amusingly informative without being unkind.

Both our parents had this interest in life, but whereas our father's was concentrated on acquiring a more far-reaching knowledge, hers was intimate and slighter and at the same time deeper. While he showed her a wider world than that of her suburban friends and her country relations, she tried to make him understand those nearer to hand. That she succeeded at all was part of her triumph.

She had a way of getting the best out of people, from her own family, husband and children to the little man with the grey moustache, who was the agent for the Metropolitan Railway, from whom for a time our house was rented. After Mother had pointed out a crack here and a mark there he would authorize new paint and paper with what the neighbours considered unfair recklessness. My father kept well out of the way on these occasions for no one ever accused him of being charming. He was too forthright and perhaps too puritanical to bother with the indirect approach.

She was a complete pushover for a hard-luck story. Beggars who came to the door were always given food and sometimes we found an unsavoury character eating a meal in front of the kitchen fire. Our father's old clothes disappeared without his permission and our house became known for a soft touch, but in those bad old days there was much hardship and her small charities were seldom undeserved. She had her regulars, sure of a kind word, a piece of bread and cheese and a cup of tea. She was seldom able to give them money as there was often pathetically little of this commodity to stretch to our needs but no one went away empty-handed. Indeed, when years later in better times, our second-hand upright piano was changed with great pride for a baby grand for our mother's birthday, the old one, when taken to pieces for removal, was found to have chalked inside it by a bygone piano-tuner:

'Ask for a glass of water here and you get a glass of beer.'

I suppose, having been a naughty child, I must have been punished. How else could I have grown up into the undoubted exemplary character I now am, but if I do not remember her beauty, I do not remember her scoldings either.

Knowing that she was on our side, as it were, we told her everything. Jack declares that had we announced we had robbed a bank she would have found excuses for us and thought it was really a worthwhile achievement merely because it was ours. My recollections of her are simply of running to her as a child, a growing girl, an adult, a middle-aged woman, to pour out my troubles, my pleasures, my hurts and disappointments and a few small successes. In this I was not alone. The people who worked for her, her friends and our friends, even the nurses who tended her in her last illness, all drew from this well of sympathetic understanding and trust which was peculiarly hers. Once when I was impatient with the boring outpourings of an uncle he justifiably reproved me.

'Your mother would have listened to me,' he said, 'and you damn well can.'

With glorious self-absorption we did not wonder if she had troubles of her own, In spite of increasing rheumatism, worry about our futures, our health or unhappiness which we were at that moment unloading upon her, and her own anxiety about the problems of retirement, we took it for granted to the end that she was happy, and perhaps she was, for I remember her laughter. She had that rare sense of the ridiculous which was not unkind, laughing with people, not at them, and she made others laugh too so that nothing, however despairing, seemed impossible to bear, and in her company an upside-down world mysteriously righted itself.

She was a marvellous and adventurous cook and as there was always someone to clear up after her, it was not until she was really old that she learnt at last to be tidy. She liked order and she achieved a measure of it, even though it was a struggle. In her last years, when she had to do all the inevitable menial jobs herself, with little and sometimes no help, she was philosophical. If we complained about her increased absence of mind she retorted, 'I know I ought to have my mind on my work. I know quite well I ought to be thinking, "This is my very own sink and therefore I am thoroughly enjoying getting out these horrid bits of goo from the plughole," but I can't. So I think of something else.'

She did what had to be done, because it was more comfortable that way, but about the dignity of labour she had misgivings. This was easy enough to discuss when it was the labour of someone else, she thought.

She did many things which infuriated my quick-tempered father. There were frenzied searches for mislaid papers, for articles hidden for safety and subsequently forgotten. She was prone to day-dreaming. Once she went out with one umbrella and came back with two, one on each arm, which she called, until it too was lost, 'The one I stole.' She denied that she was untidy, teasing my father and alleging that if a button came off his pyjamas in the night he would get up and change. He was easily irritated and his rage could be swift and sometimes awful but it was always short-lived and resolved by a hug. It was understood that anything likely to arouse this ire must be kept from him, but from her we kept nothing and she did not betray us. She never met him on the mat with a story of our misdeeds and the day's woes. It was he who had the woes. All the worries of the office and the factory would be poured out to her before he had hung up his hat.

'You'll feel better when you've had dinner, dear,' was all she ever said.

Although she was not as strict as our father she was not to be wheedled. 'No' meant 'No', and could not be turned into a 'Yes' or even 'Perhaps'. This gave us, when viewed with hindsight, a peaceful sense of security. When we were bad at least we knew we were being bad, and when we were denied something we submitted to her edict because we realized, after a few rebellious murmurs, or even tears, that it was no good persisting. It was useless to quote other children's more lenient parents.

'More fools they,' said my father. The reply was terse but remained valid.

'No one can have everything,' said my mother more gently, but with equal truth. Keeping up with the Joneses was not part of her philosophy, and in time we came to regard our deprivations as inevitable, possibly because other children seemed to think our life was also something to be envied, as perhaps it was.

'To hold is to let go,' she used to say as we grew up and she let us both go, still held to her by long invisible threads. That she often agonized over our adventures and troubles was hidden from us by our glorious egoism. Whether she was content with her lot, who can tell? When we were small she had no vote and she sometimes entertained an alarming woman with a moustache, who sat in our father's chair and told her how downtrodden she was. We gathered the visitor was something called a suffragette. Because our mother could not help being welcoming and kind she came often and stayed a long time, leaving behind a pile of tracts about Votes for Women. We all became a little tired of her, even my mother.

How much of this philosophy sank in one does not know. My mother would not have chained herself to railings or burnt her bra, but she was aware of her rights and in her own way she achieved them.

IO

I see you, a child
In a garden sheltered for buds and playtime,
Listening as if beguiled.

C. Day Lewis

It seems in retrospect that our father did not treat us as children at all. He expected us to share his adult interests and we came, perforce, to do so. With him we gazed at antique shops looking for old furniture and searched barrows in markets, which might and often did produce bargains in the way of brass and china. With him we peered into every chemist's shop, looking at the big coloured bottles which they then displayed, while he told us of his pill-pounding days. Old buildings, with their different styles of architecture, were pointed out to us and there was never a church to be passed without a visit – rood screens – bench ends. We were shown the houses where famous people had lived just as we were living, and as we faced them, their books came alive. Somehow we came to love pictures. Perhaps because he allowed himself so little leisure everything was received in small doses, pleasures were snatched in fleeting moments and boredom was thus kept at bay. When I was eighteen he took me to Dresden, where I was to learn German, and during the three busy days he stayed there with me he gave me more of the real feel of the place than I acquired in the twelve months which followed, showing me the view from the August Bridge, taking me round the Zwinger in the moonlight; walking with me through the beautiful centre of the city with its green copper roofs shining in the winter

77

sunshine; sharing all that he himself enjoyed. It was probably no more than that and when he took me to see the Gemälde Galerie it was for his own pleasure also.

'I always look at the Sistine Madonna when I come here,' he told me and together we turned into the gallery, walking smartly through it, ignoring everything until we came to the room where Raphael's huge picture hung quite by itself on a background of black velvet. People crept in with us, not speaking; even my father relaxed and did not look at his watch, and we all stayed in silence for a long time while the gentle Madonna seemed to float in space with the Babe in her arms. There was a strange atmosphere of near idolatry.

'There,' he said, when we emerged on to the cobbled square, having seen almost nothing else, 'that's the way to see pictures. Now you won't have indigestion.'

But on the way out he had stopped to show me a small portrait of a young man by An Unknown Artist. He examined it carefully and made me do this also, explaining to me why he had, for some time, thought it was by Franz Hals. When, a few years later the experts agreed with him that the artist who had painted 'The Laughing Cavalier' had also painted this portrait, we were not surprised. As a woman who worked for us once said, 'He do seem to know most things,' and he did. She had been brought in to do the cooking in some domestic emergency and she asked him how long she should boil a ham. When my mother enquired why she should think he could give her the answer to such a question she made her famous reply, famous because like most families – our critics say more than most families – we have a store of sayings dredged up from bygone incidents which became self-explanatory.

To Jack and me he did seem to know most things.

He had no eye for ball games and he danced without enthusiasm because he did it badly and knew it, but he kept himself fit by swimming, rowing and fearful exercises with iron dumb-bells and Indian clubs which we could hardly move. Although to the end of his days his pallor made him look delicate he had enormous strength, being able to lift heavy suitcases with one finger. A playful pinch from him was liable to bruise and he was teased by Rose and Lily, who asserted he could pull out a nail without pincers. Maybe he could. We were prepared to believe anything of this superman. Perhaps it is just as well he did not indulge in corporal punishment, having himself suffered from it both at home and at school. Once, however, it was considered that Jack's sins could be punished in no other way. My father fetched his walking stick and took his son across his knee. As usual my protests as an onlooker of this frightful scene were louder than Jack's, for although I was often its cause I never could bear him to be in trouble. My mother hovered in the background while my father took a deep rasping breath and raised his arm.

'Daddy,' said Jack, looking at him with interest, 'you're roaring like a lion.'

The stick was put away.

Stupidity enraged him more than actual sin and when we ran to our mother complaining that we were misunderstood she comforted us with sympathy.

'If you had been really stupid,' she said (after her usual 'Never mind!') 'he'd have drowned you at birth.'

This made us laugh because, of course, we knew he loved us and we were not unwanted kittens, yet in her mocking words lurked an element of truth. His own mind worked quickly and his family were expected to keep up with it.

Few of his generation believed in praise and it was never given, at least to our faces, and when, in 1943, I telephoned to tell him my first attempt at a novel had been accepted he merely asked if the contract had been signed.

'Well, no,' I had to admit. 'They want another five thousand words, but that will be easy.'

Of course it would be easy, I thought, feeling like Shakespeare and Dickens combined, with never a hint of possible failure, a sensation, one must add, which has never been repeated.

My father was less confident.

'Let me know when it is signed,' was all he said.

I started at once, regardless of two women and a baby, who were staying with me, and when I had finished and the contract really was there before my eyes, long and full of strange legal phrases, but still enormously exciting, I took it to him. He read it all through carefully and in silence.

'Yes,' he said at last. 'It seems all right but I should ask Hal to vet it,' Hal being my barrister brother-in-law.

I went home enraged and dampened in spite of my mother's soft words.

'He is very proud and pleased really,' she said, and so he must have been, for he opened the last bottle of champagne which he was saving for the peace.

But by then I had gone.

Behind our backs he could be, I was later told, just as tedious about our alleged talents as the next parent. Later on he was likely to force his friends to buy copies of this modest first effort, a simple tale and unlikely reading for hard-headed business men. One of these actually had the temerity to point out a misprint. My father had, I suspect, done no more than riffle through it himself or his eagle eye would have already seen this. He was never likely to miss a defect of any kind and would embrace you with fervour after an absence of some months before announcing, 'You are starting a spot on your nose.' Then, as he had never stopped being a chemist at heart, he told you what to do about it. This harsh treatment could well have been right for his daughter, apt at times to dart away in day-dreams of success and glory far beyond her capacities and unlikely to be achieved. It was as well there was someone to drag me back to the cold world of reality, but Jack, although a handsome and clever boy, having inherited his father's brains and his mother's looks, had also inherited her diffidence. He would have benefited from a little praise.

It was not that he did not appreciate Jack's talents, but my father was seldom able to express it aloud. He could put this on paper, for like all his family he wrote letters which were longer than his speeches, and one day, just before he died, he wrote in praise of his son.

But he addressed the letter to me and not to Jack.

My father could be raspingly sarcastic, mincing no words and sometimes his terseness might wound, yet this direct manner had its own attraction as those who lived with him and worked with him found. If he offended, and he often did, our mother was there to soften the blow, for she was not so much behind him as part of him. She knew, both personally and by repute, the workers in the factory and the office. The foreigners with whom he did business were not entertained in restaurants on expense accounts, but in our own home. They brought their wives to our house and sometimes stayed with us; as the years went by we also stayed with them. In search of business he travelled to new countries with strange-sounding names and altered frontiers, Czechoslovakia, Jugoslavia, a smaller Austria and Germany. We listened to talk about Sudetenland, the Polish Corridor, Alsace-Lorraine, as aspects of their problems were explained and we grew up to hear all shades of political opinion, to question such matters as the Treaty of Versailles, the problems of labour relations. Thus we came to know about a wider world, so that when I married into a well-known legal family I was amazed, in spite of their witty conversation, at what seemed to me to be the narrowness of their horizons. For all that, my father was a good Tory and 'good' is the word to describe him, for he believed in the thrifty and independent standards of his own spartan youth.

In spite of their being completely different in every way, our parents weathered the storms, for I cannot believe that an irritable man, who suffered later from gout, did not produce them, but if so, they were not overheard by us. There were periods of financial anxiety, illnesses, worries great and small, yet all we remember is laughter. They used to call me their 'Undutiful Daughter' and so I fear, unintentionally, I must have been, making their lives anxious with, amongst other cares, a long and supposedly fatal disease, but although she listened to other people's troubles my mother never spoke of her own.

Children are certain cares, but uncertain comforts.

Latin proverb

For the whole of our childhood and youth we were also blessed by the presence of Elsie. She came when Jack was a baby and she loved him as her own. In me she was able to see faults but Jack remained perfect in her eyes and she was not above concealing such misdemeanours as leaving his toys out all night or walking over 'her clean floor with muddy boots'. Her arrival was, my mother often said, the luckiest thing which ever happened to us.

When my mother left Worcestershire for the wilder shores of London my grandmother wrote awful warnings of all 'servants' applying for employment whose antecedents were unknown. Unless they had familiar pedigrees my grandmother suspected them of coming straight out of reformatories or worse and she did not understand that in London it was difficult to know the details of their families, which she thought essential. But no one could disapprove of Elsie and she was the envy of the neighbourhood. She came from what was then a remote village in Buckinghamshire. Her mother had been a cook and her father was a carpenter on a local estate. She was extremely intelligent and although she had left school at thirteen she wrote well and descriptively in a clear hand. She was an avid reader and, being the eldest of twelve, she was good with children as well as skilled in all the domestic arts. More than that, she was something very welcome at that time. She was economical. During the Great War she made appetizing meals out of nothing, luscious cakes with two and a half currants and no eggs; toffee and jam with a stretched sugar ration and a dish, mostly vegetables, with only a fleeting brush with the meat ration, which we branded with her name. We called it Elsie Stew. All this she taught my mother, who now needed such economies. Scrambling between them I absorbed these also and they emerged from the background of memory to be useful in World War Two.

When Elsie came back from her occasional weekends in her home she was laden with produce from her father's garden and boiling over with news of her vast family and all the characters in her village. These she could imitate in a way which kept us enthralled for hours. Our greatest treat, a reward for exceptional goodness, was 'tea-in-the-kitchen-with-Elsie'. There was no misbehaviour. Woe betide anyone so ungenteel as to talk with a mouthful of cake, or to forget a 'please' or a 'thank you'. Our friends appreciated her also and our friends' mothers even more.

She was pretty with bright blue eyes and curly auburn hair and there was at one time some rumour of an admirer. But although she was an enormous talker (the only vice she had, my father said, when he tired of her echoing chatter) she kept her disappointment, if disappointment it was, to herself. Nothing came of her expectations and in our selfishness we were not sorry.

She earned eighteen pounds a year, rising gradually to fifty, extravagant sums which made both my grandmothers blench at the outrageous wages which had to be paid in London. We were grown up when she had to leave us to live with her parents and the ones who came after were never quite the same. How could they be? She was a bulwark of our childhood and when she left we felt as if there had been a death. Had she lived today we should never have known her in this way. She would certainly have gone to a university and made a name for herself in a wider sphere, but for her generation that sphere was perforce circumscribed within the limits of our affections.

83

When she was old and both my parents were dead I went to visit her to see her new bungalow. She wanted to hear news of everybody, all the clan of our friends and relatives, every birth, marriage and death.

'Those years spent with you all were the happiest of my life,' she said.

'But how could they be?' I asked. 'There was the war and not a single labour-saving device and terribly low wages.'

'It was such a happy house,' she said. 'Mind you, your father was particular. He set great store by things being . . . right. He could be awkward, your father, very awkward.'

She smiled as she remembered his 'awkwardness'.

'But he did so love your mother,' she added. 'He really did. You could feel it right through the house – a kind of happiness.'

She showed me the modest building where she had received her education.

'You ought to have gone to a university,' I said. 'If you had been born later, you would have done.'

We were walking up the street to the churchyard and she showed me where her parents and grandparents were buried and where she also was to lie shortly afterwards.

There was no resentment in her voice when she agreed.

'Of course,' she said. No more.

Despite her red hair Elsie was never one for carrying banners.

The Land of the Pinn River

12

Recollect the elm-trees misty
And the footpaths climbing twisty
Under cedar-shaded palings,
Low laburnum leaned on railings
Out of Northolt on and upwards to the
heights of Harrow hill.

Sir John Betjeman

Although we boasted to our country relations that we lived
in London, making it sound as if the King and Queen were
near neighbours and we could see the Houses of Parliament
from our windows, Pinner, where our parents lived modestly
in a semi-detached house owned by the Metropolitan
Railway, was in those days in deep country. My mother,
house-hunting in 1912, had chosen it because, although it
was only a dozen miles from Marble Arch, at Pinner she
could hear the larks.

The railway line in those days ran between fields. From
our back windows there was then a distant view of the green
slopes rising to Nower Hill. There were scattered, sedate
Victorian villas, with names like Mon Repos or Firgrove
(which was our kindergarten), but the house in which we
lived was new and we were its first occupants. It was the
small creeping beginning of speculative building, which in
time turned the whole area into the faceless desert of
Metroland.

In my bedroom at night, when Elsie drew back the
curtains, the lights of the passing trains flickered by a
mysterious optical illusion round the walls. Sometimes, when
the little house was overfull, and it often was, I was given a
camp bed elsewhere. The temporary occupant of my bed
did not enjoy either the flickering lights or the rumble of the

trains. We were near the station and the clank clank of shunting trucks in the siding during the early hours, which only partially woke me and then soothed me to sleep again, did no such thing to them.

Although the splendid new electric trains of the Metropolitan lines to Baker Street and the City, and the more exciting steam expresses which ran into Marylebone, took us to the heart of London in less than twenty minutes, we could be and indeed we were brought up mainly as country children, following the seasons with our parents or Elsie, as they had done in their own childhoods; searching the lanes for the first celandine; Ruislip woods for bluebells and dog violets; Cuckoo Hill for primroses and the rare cowslip; Pinner woods for blackberries, crab apples and sloes and Woodridings for glossy conkers. Many of these expeditions involved miles of walking, the grown-ups laden with picnic baskets and bottles of lemonade. We were often accompanied by other children, for Elsie was something of a Pied Piper and to encourage us on these endurance marches, she converted them into semi-military operations. She formed the Robin Hood Club. Our panama hats were pinned up on one side and adorned with a pheasant's feather. We were equipped with small haversacks as a sly method of making us help with the transport and off we stamped, singing all the way, proud of the fact that the wounded soldiers in blue from the hospital at the Grove saluted us as we passed by. Whole unforgettable days were spent in Ruislip woods. This was not a small remnant of something called the Green Belt, tamed by golf courses, but a spreading forest, miles from any sign of habitation.

Pinner village, of which mere traces now remain, had only a handful of shops, some large attractive old houses and a few farms, surrounded by fields and woodland and watered by the then undisciplined River Pinn. We did not know that the ponds, where we caught our tadpoles and fed the ducks, would be filled in and houses built on them, that the meandering Pinn, where we paddled, would be restrained

88

by concrete and the hedges, where we picked blackberries and looked for birds' nests, would be obliterated, or that the trees, which shaded our walks, would be cut down.

With the march of progress the charm of the lanes with their little bridges and solitary farms was eventually asphalted out of memory. Such attractions of Pinner as remain, the High Street and its old houses climbing up the hill to the church with its cross on the top of the tower, have been saved by the public spirit of a few earlier citizens led by the help and generosity of one man, who protested with some success in an unprotesting age.

At the Queen's Head there was a performing bear, a sad, chained animal who executed cumbrous dancing steps for our amusement, in a manner which did not then strike our unawakened consciences as inhumane. Once a week we gave a penny to a man with a barrel organ and on the Wednesday after Whit Monday there was Pinner Fair, which still persists. Due to an ancient charter of which everyone was proud, it took place in the streets, so that for twenty-four hours Pinner village was completely blocked with roundabouts and swings, sideshows, coconut shys and pressing humanity. All the schools had a half-holiday. The night before the fair the caravans arrived at sundown and by dawn on the day after they had to be gone, so that nothing remained of the brief orgy but the rubbish which blew about the gutters and into the gardens.

There was a certain amount of fright infused into the excitement of the fair, for we were not allowed to leave Elsie's side and had to be back by tea-time, when we were told it started to be too rough for us. I believe today it can be even rougher, but in those days in the afternoons we surrendered ourselves to a fearful glimpse of paradise.

Would we really be stolen by gypsies if we let go of Elsie's hand and was it better to have two cheap rides on the small roundabout or one expensive fling on the big one, whose cheerful steam organ could be heard when we lay on our beds, too excited to sleep?

The picturesque village was then still the haunt of artists.

Bert Thomas lived there with his tribe of children, taking them for outings packed in a governess cart. His drawings in *Punch* made our familiar backgrounds famous. Heath Robinson contrived his fantastic machines in a house in Waxwell Lane. The lanes, Moss, Love, Chapel, Cannons and Rayners really were lanes and you really could hear the cuckoo on Cuckoo Hill. There were farms where we saw cows milked by hand and bought unhygienic cream and if one climbed above Nower Hill there were the spreading fields of Harrow Weald, just as Anthony Trollope had described them in *Orley Farm*.

In the winter, when the waterlogged London clay made the field paths and woods impassable, we were restricted to the roads and lanes but this was no hardship for there was little traffic; we could bowl our hoops recklessly down the hills and there were the delicious thrills of standing on the small bridges and watching our sticks borne along on the raging torrent which winter had made of the River Pinn, or of staring through the iron fence at the waterfall cascading down from the artificial lake at the end of Paines Lane. The road walks were as full of interest as the fields and woods. There was the bridge at Hatch End where the steam train thundered up through the midlands to Holyhead, to catch the boat to Ireland. Moor Park, now full of mock-millionaire houses surrounding a golf course, was an unfettered landscape where the trees, we were told, had been decapitated by the sorrowing Duchess of Monmouth when her husband was executed for his part in the ill-fated Monmouth rebellion. Everywhere had its own near fairy-tale. Harefield, then an isolated and lonely village, boasted a cottage where Nicolas, the only English Pope, was born and in Pinner woods was the house where the man who wrote *The Last Days of Pompeii* had lived. It was an attractive place with a little bridge over a stream. One day, our father said, he would buy our mother just such a house. We would hang over strange gates admiring gardens. It would be one like this or one like that, he said. He never quite achieved what he had in mind but he went a long way towards it, and she was content.

The mellow buildings of Harrow School, topped by the spire, rose in the mist from the surrounding fields. In winter they were waterlogged but in summer, before they were drained and obliterated by houses, to become the district known as North Harrow and Kenton, London sprawled no farther than Wembley. One could, and we often did, walk all the way to Harrow from Pinner, across these damp meadows full of cuckoo spit and kingcups. We would climb the Hill and sit in the churchyard dreaming dreams just as Byron had done a century earlier. The old red brick houses which made up Harrow School were an isolated living unit like a medieval abbey.

We knew one of the masters because he came from Worcestershire and sometimes we were asked to tea. We climbed the hill from the station and suddenly there were all those strange animals, hats tip-tilted, battling with that menace of my youth, elastic, just as I battled, knotting it when it perished, adjusting it, perhaps even hating it as much as I did.

Mr Hughes had a small house where he took a few special pupils in those days considered unsuitable to be embroiled in the hurly-burly of school life. Thus a gentle brown-skinned boy, who was afterwards King of Siam, would pass me the bread and butter, or the crisp-haired future Shah of Persia would ask me how old I was and where I went to school. We went to that unforgettable experience, the School Sing Song, and heard the roar of breaking voices, and watched some of the men in the audience, bald or white-haired, stand up and be counted as Old Harrovians, when it came to 'Forty Years On', a ditty which has the same sentimental nostalgia of time and place as the 'Eton Boating Song' or 'Ilkla Moor Bah't Hat' or 'The Oak and the Ash'.

The other Harrow at the bottom of the hill was our nearest town. It had a penny bazaar, an enterprise from the inventive brain of a man named Marks, and though it was a long way from the present green and gold splendours of Marks and Spencer, it had the same honey-pot attraction, the same terrible way of making one want more than the money in one's pocket would buy. Sixpence did not go far enough and shop-lifting was a crime comparable with murder. How far our honesty was produced by fear of the police, by fear of our father's wrath, or ultimate hell-fire I do not know, but even I, capable of inventive crime, did not consider shop-lifting as a game to play on Saturday afternoons.

Of necessity we grew up to be capable of walking what would nowadays be considered immense distances. Our parents were walkers, Elsie was a walker and sometimes, as a special outing, we all took the train to the outback of Rickmansworth or Chorleywood and from there explored the rolling commonland and hills of the Chilterns. At Chenies we were told of the Dukes of Bedford who were buried in the strange tombs in the little church. Afterwards we might, as a great treat, have tea at the Bedford Arms, eaten at a big table covered with a white cloth and Jack and I sat on a horsehair-covered sofa, which scratched that sensitive crease of flesh between the shin bone and the knee, which was unprotected by socks or knickers. We bore this bravely, for we were scolded for wriggling and the lavish tea – home-made cakes and watercress – was worth a certain amount of suffering. It was a set tea costing no more than a shilling and from us they could have made little, for we were bent on getting our money's worth and were always capable of clearing everything but a last crumb left for manners. In spite of this the proprietress would welcome us as we arrived to fortify ourselves for the long trek home in the dark, while our parents talked about the Flying Duchess and the Bedford tombs and the beautiful house near the church which was so often empty. So unenlightened were we that it did not occur to us to envy the Duke. The acceptance of the old order may have been unthinking and perhaps stupid but it made it possible to enjoy his watercress, which we ate with relish at the inn named after him, without worrying about the rights and wrongs of our place in the complex scheme of social order.

13

Smoothly from Harrow, passing Preston Road,
They saw the last green fields and misty sky.

Sir John Betjeman

Two or three times a year we went 'to Town'. That is to say
we took the train from Pinner (steam if possible because the
electric ones made us travel-sick), emerging at Baker Street
or Marylebone. From there we would ride to Oxford Circus
on the open top of a bus in order to buy our school clothes at
Peter Robinson's or Liberty's, ending the expedition with
tea in the dark respectability of Buzzards'. Should our
mother be in funds we would lunch grandly at the new
Regent Palace, where waiters flourished a three-course
menu and there was a BAND; all this for little more than the
cost today of a first-class letter. How was it done? Besides
the genius of Joe Lyons, some sweated labour must regret-
tably be assumed. It was unnoticed by us as we allowed
ourselves to be bowed to our table. But neither did we notice
the sweated labour of our parents. Our mother had probably
sewn until late into the night making the dress which I was
wearing and our father – he really had sweated to produce
the wherewithal for our luxurious luncheon.

Occasionally he would say, 'I want things to be better
for Jack and you than they were for me,' and this he
accomplished, but I was grown up before I appreciated how
it was achieved. On weekdays he was out of the house by
eight and did not return until after we were in bed. The
great day was Saturday when he came back at three o'clock,
laden with treasures bought at Leadenhall Market, oranges,

93

apples and perhaps a chicken or a lobster. We would hang round him to see what he had brought and our mother would chide him for his extravagance. I could never bear this, even though I knew that she only half meant it.

Until he had a severe illness, due largely to overwork, during our childhood his holidays were scarce and brief. As a young man, learning to be a chemist, and later practising as one, pounding away at his pestle and mortar, sometimes below ground in a basement dispensary, a slave to the emergency bell at nights and weekends, he seldom saw the daylight. Because there was no other way of achieving his ambitions he was often studying when he should have been playing, but he had a passion for the theatre and the music hall and he told us that, owing to the long hours he had worked as a young man, he could only see the end of any entertainment. This he had turned to an advantage, as by arriving half-way through a performance, he was allowed in at half-price. Thus he could afford more frequent visits. He knew all the old songs and these, suitable and unsuitable, he sang to us when we invaded his bed on Sunday mornings.

'You really shouldn't . . . ' our mother would reprove when she brought his weekend treat, breakfast in bed. We absorbed these ditties as we absorbed other items of our upbringing. Sir Winston Churchill, I am told, also sang these songs to his children. He and my father were both born in the same year and although so different in circumstance and education they were both the product of another age and they had the same characteristics, a dogged determination, a capacity for work combined with a special kind of resilience in adversity, and also an impatience with others who were not of a similar mind. This resilience my father often needed, for his business depended on foreign trade and he had to weather two world wars with the disastrous thirties in between. He would pour out his despair to my mother and seemingly dispose of it, for in a few days, whatever the disaster, he would have a clear view of the future and a confidence that the troubles could be surmounted, as indeed they always were.

Our parents were really immigrants from the country, now living in London, and like all immigrants they had a certain good-tempered scorn for their roots, and, unlike their children and grandchildren, no thought of returning other than for brief visits. In the early part of the century there were many men who had come to London to make their fortunes. By their own efforts they became members of the professions, merchants and bankers, press barons and politicians. Some of them became millionaires, some of them must have failed and within this range there were a number of men like my father and his friends, who had come a long way from their beginnings and made a modest success of their lives, providing for others when they died. At any Guildhall dinner there were traces of country burrs, Scottish and Welsh lilts and aggressive northern accents, all overlaid by a London veneer, so that it was often hard to tell whence they came. From their country roots they had arrived with few advantages, other than ambition and a capacity for solid work, which had a morality of its own. It was a time when, despite terrible world conditions, hope was seldom lost, for brains and toil and a little luck brought their own rewards. It never occurred to my father that this might not always be so and such success as he had he enjoyed. He became a Freeman of the City of London and sat on the court of his company, walking in procession in his fur-trimmed robe with great pride. In 1940, after the raid when the Sacred Mile burnt from end to end, so that the red glare in the sky could be seen from his house in Bucking-hamshire, tears streamed down his cheeks. Perhaps his emotions were the same as his father-in-law's when he showed us Cromwell's bullet holes in the walls of Powick church.

'Barbarians!' was the word they both used. No one said that war was barbarous in itself, for they had never thought it so. It was then that my father became unforgiving, even when the beauty of Dresden, which he and I had so dearly loved, was also destroyed by our own bombers. His capacity for seeing both points of view was now severely challenged. Between the wars he had been prepared to think that the

Germans were perhaps misled by the evil Hitler and the British were partially at fault for allowing this to happen. He could even argue about earlier mistakes in world policy which had made the horrors of Hitler inevitable, but the burning of his own patch, the City of London, he was never able to forgive.

How much his capacity for overcoming difficulties and surviving setbacks which would have finished another man, was due to our mother, I do not know. Indeed, as a child I was not aware of any special anxiety and there must have been many. I realized at that time that we were not well off but I was blind to what must have been periods of sheer self-denial on the part of our parents, for in many ways we seemed to have more fun than other children.

Our father had been brought up in an inhospitable household so that he always welcomed visitors, whether his own relations or those of our mother, or later Jack's and my friends. The inadequate house burst at the seams. Neither of our parents seemed aware that it had deficiencies and compared unfavourably with those of our friends' homes, nor did they consider the simplicity of our life needed any apology; indeed no apology was needed, for ours was the house where we all met and played and the relations from the country, on visits to the wonders of London, kept our spare bedroom in constant use.

During the week our father was seldom more than a voice downstairs or a face behind the newspaper at breakfast. In the evenings he was always late, being a congenital misser of trains and when once absorbed in his work, time simply was not. If he was not home by twenty to eight then it would be twenty past eight or even twenty to nine, his delays being punctuated by the well-known intervals of the Metropolitan Railway; his dinner went back into the oven and we were sent to bed. The weekends were different. They had a special quality because from three o'clock on Saturday until we went to bed on Sunday evening he belonged to us and, urged by our mother and Elsie and not unmindful of his quick temper, we made enormous efforts to be good. His wrath when roused was sufficient to cow us, at least momentarily. Nothing ever cowed us permanently. We accepted our scoldings for taking our second-hand tricycle (which Jack and I jointly owned) to pieces and then endangering health and limb by riding it after we had put it together upside down in a more interesting position. We promised not to do this again, a promise we kept, for by that time we were engaged in making gunpowder in the back garden, with a fervour and ingenuity which would have qualified us for any revolutionary movement.

'What have they been doing today?' my father asked as usual and my mother said we had been quite good, but rather noisy, as she took his hat and hung it on the hall stand, that useful monster of Edwardian furniture with its box for gloves and its pegs submerged in coats.

In all innocence she explained, 'They bought some powders and mixed it all together and kept hitting it with your hammer. Oh! The hammer is all right,' she added with haste, for tools so often borrowed were apt to suffer in our hands. 'They brought it back and I saw that they put it away. It kept them amused for the whole day.'

Our father examined the powder and questioned us, and then went off to give the chemist who had sold the ingredients a piece of his mind. He might be short-tempered but he was always fair. We promised that we would never again make explosives and we have not done so.

On Saturday evenings, when other men went to the local, he always took me to the village to pay the paper bill and choose the library books for the weekend. We also bought a small box of chocolates for my mother and a quarter of a pound of Mackintosh's toffees for Jack and me. Perhaps the recipe has not changed over the years, but nothing has ever tasted the same since those far-off days. Not that we ate them all at once or even had right of access to the bag. With all the stealth of Santa Claus two toffees were put by our bed while we slept. They were known as our 'surprise'. Somehow a 'surprise' and Mackintosh's toffee came to mean the same thing, like the kiss and the thimble in *Peter Pan*. It also ensured a certain period of peace for our parents on Sunday mornings as part of the bargain. The procedure of the disposal of the toffee papers was also laid down in no uncertain terms. It was understood that to leave them lying about either inside or outside the house was a mortal sin and not to be contemplated, for it would elicit the well-known bellow and might even mean no 'surprise' the following week, although by then there was always the chance that the whole episode might be forgotten. Our father's rages, though swift and alarming at the time, especially when in later years he suffered from gout, were short-lived. Somehow, even at an early age, we knew that his bark was worse than his bite.

Perhaps because he was often tired, even exhausted, he could not bear noise and we grew up to dislike it also. We were never fond of children who went mad with over-excitement. The weekend for us was the time when our father was at home and it was an oasis of quiet, setting it apart from the hurry of the week. Not dull, merely different.

I do not remember that on Sundays time hung heavily on our hands. It was a day for walking, for reading, for going to church, for 'Birds, Beasts and Fishes' and 'Consequences'. Card games such as 'Happy Families' were only later considered other than immoral on Sundays. How God became gradually more broadminded I do not know and did not question. In fact, on looking back one realizes how little was questioned. We sang hymns and a selection of the tunes, which my mother fished out of the music stool; Teresa del Riego's setting of 'A Child's Garden of Verses', which our mother played.

My be-ed is-s like
A li-ittle boat,
Nurse tucks me in
When I embark.

But no nurse tucked us in. On Sundays there was not even Elsie who was doubtless also singing in Emmanuel Church, Northwood, where she walked every week, and our mother was too busy with the latest novel out of the library, Charles Garvice or Arnold Bennett, Ian Hay or H. G. Wells, Ethel

M. Dell or Galsworthy. Her taste was all-embracing, uncritical and catholic. If by any chance some music was being coaxed out of the cat's-whisker wireless set which our father, of all men the most unmechanically minded, had later been one of the first to buy, we knew that, although we were by then in our teens, even a creaking stair as we crept to bed might bring down wrath on our heads.

Often there were weekend visitors and we went to bed to the music of Rachmaninov or Lehar, according to who was performing. Everyone could play the piano more or less, some rather less than more, but this did not stop them. From my bedroom above I could hear their laughter and their conversation rumbling below and once when they were all sitting under the trellis arbour, which was covered by a sooty rose, there was so much hilarity that I could bear it no longer and hung out of the window to see what was going on.

The sight which met my eyes nearly killed me with horror. My mother was being taught to smoke.

For a long time I hugged the knowledge of this unspeakable sin to my as yet non-existent bosom, to join all the other chill fears which inexplicably assailed me from time to time, and as inexplicably vanished.

14

I have seen flowers come in stony places
And kind things done by men with ugly faces
And the gold cup won by the worst horse at the races,
So I trust too.

John Masefield

Although I do not remember severe punishments we were often in disgrace. The blanket of disapproval which descended was black and all-embracing and there was no way of escaping it until it had run its course. Then suddenly it was lifted. One had said one was sorry, as indeed by that time one was, one was kissed and forgiven, told to be good in future and I did try, I did indeed. At least I did not repeat the same crime but my ideas were far-reaching and unpredictable.

That Jack was four years younger made no difference. He was dragged along with the rest of us until he was able to think up projects of his own. Although these were often as devastating as mine, by the mere fact of making less noise about them, he often escaped just retribution. I would announce what I had in mind, and on being told that it would not be allowed, I would argue. Then I would be told I was being cheeky and I would retire momentarily vanquished, in a flood of tears, and already in disgrace for creating a scene, before any other misdemeanour had actually been committed. Jack was wiser. He quietly went off with his cronies and was only in trouble when he was found out. The injustice of this should have soured our relations at an early age. Yet it did not do so and we remain devoted to this day. He sometimes thinks I am rather trying and I also think he can be rather trying, but to our spouses we present a solid front against all attack, despite the fact that we are not in the least alike. Jack is cleverer than I, a better organizer, a more systematic worker. He is a perfectionist. What he does has to be efficiently achieved and right and if he sees that this is not within his powers he does not embark on the adventure of a plunge into attempted disaster. Now I am all for 'Everything Once' and 'Let's Have a Bash'. G. K. Chesterton's advice, 'If a thing is worth doing, it is worth doing badly' is my motto. Jack has a firmness of resolve which was then called obstinacy and deplored as much as my tendency to argue. When we were children no one thought that either of these defects might be useful in adult life and in vain our elders tried to bring us to mend our ways.

Without knowing how it happened we learnt to read. Just before I went to school in a blinding flash I realized as I sat on the floor in front of the fire, that I could really read. The words were making pictures in my mind, not my words but other people's. The book was Beatrix Potter's *The Pie and the Patty-pan*. It was a moment of illumination and magic never to be forgotten. I was nearly six, not then considered at all forward for such an accomplishment. Jack, however, could read and write and count by the time he was four and I was so proud of his accomplishments that I boasted about him at the kindergarten which I attended and which he, as yet, did not. (On looking back I fear I must have been much given to boasting.) Thus is was that when Jack joined me at Firgrove he was not put with the babies but with veterans of seven and eight. Moreover I had said he eould add up and this was not strictly accurate. As usual my wishful fantasies had embellished fact and Jack on his first day at school, overcome by the mathematical problem of making two and two into four, took evasive action. He asked if he might be 'excused' and from the other side of the room I was called forth to show him the way. He emerged resolute from the lavatory, stood in the passage where our coats and shoebags were hanging and announced that he was going home.

I was aghast. I tried to drag him back into the classroom

but it was useless. Jack had a way of planting his feet and clinging to the nearest object, in this case the staircase, which defied removal. He was quite quiet about all this. He did not argue as I might have done or cry as I certainly should have done, for my tears flowed freely and often. He simply refused to go back, and then, as usual, I, having cried and argued, was the one in disgrace, while Jack was cajoled back to the classroom by the assistant mistress, with a promise that he should not be required to add up just yet.

By such simple means he often won.

One day he decided, why, no one knows – but he was a child who had terrors he could not explain and they were doubtless misunderstood – that he would not go to drill. Something had put him off the idea. Drill was an extra and took place on Friday afternoons in the Baptist Hall in Paines Lane. We were about to set off to walk there with Elsie when Jack said 'No'. He was already in his sailor coat and hat with his gymn shoes in a bag when he decided against it. He was exactly like a horse refusing a jump. Rose, who was staying with us, our mother and Elsie all tried to manhandle him along the front path on his bottom. At the gate they had to acknowledge defeat and it was admitted that even three grown-ups could not drag him a quarter of a mile. After a fearful but noiseless struggle, watched with fascinated horror by four passers-by, they gave up. I was the one who cried and I was the one who went to drill. To this day no one knows why Jack behaved in this way and all that he can remember of the incident is the shocked expressions of some children in the window of the house on the opposite side of the road.

For some unjust reason the mob of children who marched with us in the Robin Hood Club were mostly boys. Thus, by not having to wear dresses, when it came to climbing trees they enjoyed some advantages. Until I was eighteen my mother made all my clothes, fitting, refitting and adjusting hems while I stood on the kitchen table being told not to stick out my stomach. There seemed always to be something wrong with my stance. 'Shoulders back!' 'Head up!' 'Look where you're going!' 'Turn out your toes!' My mother gave audible sighs at having to fit an inadequate pattern on to a monstrosity. She learnt as she went along, for she had no one to teach her; patterns were difficult to follow and there were no dressmaking classes laid on by a helpful society. Her standards were high so she pinned and tried on and tacked and unpicked and repinned on my protesting form, and in the end I was as well dressed as my fellows. Jack, from the age of six, wore 'bought' clothes, a reason for dark envy, for I was not grateful for her efforts and longed passionately for 'bought' clothes also.

She was not a hoarder but amongst the things I found when she died was a tiny blue tunic, embroidered in red, the last garment of babyhood she had made for her son, and with it a small distorted object in the blue and brown colours of the preparatory school which he attended when he was eight.

It was his first school cap.

In spite of my growing like a young hop, as my grandfather said, my own clothes, when I had finished with them, were seldom useful for anything but rubbing rags and quite properly no sentiment was wasted on them. I tore them, I covered them with mud, spilt milk on them; even worse, I grew out of them. Everything was made with a double hem which was let down and let down again. I never became fatter, merely longer.

For her day my mother had ideas ahead of her time. Instead of the frilly knickers worn by my contemporaries, I had bloomers which matched my dresses. My knees were seldom out of bandages. Somehow my long legs flew about in all directions when I ran and finally knotted themselves so that I fell, in the manner of Tom Webster's cartoon of Tishy. It was not so much that I knocked into things as that they always seemed to be in my way. To me it felt as if inanimate objects actually attacked me.

'The elephant is a graceful bird,' sighed my father, overlooking the fact that it was from him I had inherited the clumsiness so much deplored.

In winter black cashmere stockings which cost four shillings and elevenpence three farthings, a subterfuge for the enormous sum of five shillings, were frequently reduced to a bloody mess, past repair, and had to be replaced. I was made aware that to clothe me was expensive although my beaver and felt hats were cast-offs of my aunts, altered hopefully, so that they might suit me, which they seldom did, by a process called re-blocking. In summer I wore a panama hat. Because these hats were cheaper untrimmed my mother ornamented them herself with ribbons to match my dresses. Once, together with an aunt, she trimmed my hat with a wreath of daisies, but this was not repeated. It was considered, rightly in spite of my pleas, that plain things were best suited to plain girls.

For a female of any age to go outside the gate without a hat was unthinkable. In winter it was supposed to stop you having earache and in summer sunstroke. This apparently it achieved, at any rate in my case. A hat appeared to be inevitable and was accepted. A dress, however, was another matter. In climbing trees and scrambling over fences and walls with Jack and his friends it seemed only a reasonable idea to remove this encumbrance and one day I took off the offending garment and hung it on a convenient branch. The sensation when Elsie discovered this strip-tease act, the hasty calling of my mother, the swift covering of my nakedness, is something I have never forgotten. If psychologists are to be believed it should have had a lasting effect on my love life. No one told me why the revelation of my skinny body, well concealed by short-sleeved combinations (as opposed to long-sleeved winter ones), plus a Liberty bodice and bloomers, to three seven-year-old boys should be such a crime. Perhaps they did not themselves know, but it was generally considered to be yet another sign that I should come to a bad end.

In spite of, or maybe because of, our lack of toys, we were never bored. Our tiny garden had an advantage over the strips of our neighbours. It was irregular. For some reason it trailed off into a corner which came to be exclusively ours, and we installed ourselves in this private territory. It must have measured no more than eight square feet, but here the boys made a dugout modelled on those of the Great War, with a wooden roof and a chimney and a fireplace on which we cooked strange messes, a forerunner of that delight in burning things out of doors, the barbecue. We constructed a tiny pond about the size of a flower pot, which we lined with London clay on the principles used by the Romans, and here we kept tadpoles and raised frogs. From the same clay we modelled objects and baked them. On the boundary of our domain a willow pole, put in by my father as a clothes post, had taken root and quickly become a tree. Here we hung a perforated tin can and we would sit for hours amongst the leaves watching evil-smelling smoke come out of its holes; or we hung upside down like bats or played acrobats and occasionally we enlivened the proceedings by damaging ourselves and having to be supplied with first aid. We still bear the scars.

In between we would watch the trains. To the envy of our friends the Metropolitan Railway ran through the cutting at the end of the garden and we could sit on the iron railings of the fence for hours, taking numbers and waving at the engine drivers whom we came to know. Had we less initiative than the children of today, that we never thought of derailing the trains or hurling bricks at the drivers? We knew them all and told the time by them, waving madly at our special ones as they went by. They always waved back; they were our friends. Now, when I have occasion to go by British Rail to Northwood and beyond, from the train window I see the scene of these adventures, our handkerchief of a garden with our own irregular corner, made even smaller by time's interval. The only sign of our former occupation is an enormous chestnut tree.

It was planted one day with great ceremony by Jack, who had grown it in a jam-jar from a bright, glossy conker. It looks as if it has been there since the beginning of the world.

15

I walk through the long school room questioning.

W. B. Yeats

The cross on the top of Pinner church was put there, we were told by the vicar, to guide travellers through the forest which, in the middle ages, surrounded it. It was once shining brass and was as long as the nave. I believed this as I then believed everything my elders told me. True or false? Who can say?

The Vicar in our day was a widower with two small boys who sat on either side of their nurse in exalted seats in the choir stalls, their angelic expressions sometimes belied by their behaviour. How I envied them in their privileged positions at the Sunday afternoon service for children, but I did my best to emulate them by sitting in the front pew beneath the pulpit, even though I feared, often with reason, that Jack would want to be taken out halfway through. For a while I was haunted by worry about the capacity of Jack's small bladder, for he suffered from a strange claustrophobic anxiety the moment he was enclosed in any space without access to a lavatory. A train without a corridor caused him to behave like a trapped animal, as he desperately looked for means of escape. Once reassured that his problem could, if necessary, be solved, he settled down and forgot about it. But at Pinner church, with no obvious convenience, it was not possible to calm his fears and sooner or later I would overcome my feeling of shame and tiptoe down the aisle with him to find a sheltered gravestone. Once we were seen and terrified by a furious woman who rushed out of her nearby house telling us we were disgusting. Yet, despite these experiences, traumatic for both of us and never confessed at home, we loved going to church, or rather we loved the Vicar. He was a man who really understood children. Indeed I felt he even understood my problems with Jack, and he probably did. The service was not a Sunday School in the accepted sense of the word, for he gave it a liturgy of its own, which never varied. There were two psalms – the twenty-third and the Nunc Dimittis – and three hymns with proper tunes we could really sing, undeterred by the fact that we did not always understand the words. Jack thought that 'Christ who once amongst us' was 'Christ who won a mongster' and pondered for some time as to what a 'mongster' could be. There was a lesson, short and out of one of the more comprehensible stretches of the Bible, a few simple and familiar prayers and a brief sermon, hopefully exhorting us to be good and suggesting ways of achieving this. There was a collection, the bag being taken round by venerable boys of ten or so, never girls, a form of sex-discrimination envied but not questioned, and then, on the way out, we were given illustrated stamps which we stuck in books so that at the end of the year we might qualify for a prize in the form of an improving religious work. There was nearly always a christening afterwards and most of us were so fervent that we stayed for this as well, Jack protesting but overruled. My main object in staying was to hear the choice of names and to see the vicar hold up the baby so that we could all have a good view of the infant, be ore the moving moment when he gave it a kiss and his blessing and handed it back duly baptized. He loved all children and they loved him.

His figure was portly and one of my friends, who had evidently been given some rudimentary sex education, asserted that she thought he was going to have a baby. This I considered unlikely and was subsequently proved to be right. Our ignorance of such matters was and continued to be abysmal. In fact we were stupid enough not to be interested. How we could remain so uninformed I cannot now imagine. Babies were born all around us but we took them as part of the scene, like regular meals and going to school. We did not connect them with the combined action of our parents.

When I was about fourteen this same friend, whose mother obviously had more advanced ideas than my mother, persuaded mine to let me accompany her daughter to a lantern lecture on the Facts of Life, which was being given in the interests of morality for the new generation. A blushing young man operated the magic lantern and my friend and I were embarrassed by this, without knowing why. The rest of the audience, who were largely maids, sent by well meaning and hopeful employers, were overcome by giggles. The lecture, as I recall, consisted of slides of rabbits. First one rabbit, then two rabbits, then lots of rabbits and there was one really horrible picture which haunted me for days, of a cross-section of a rabbit with little rabbits inside, all neatly sliced in half. As we walked home together we confided to each other that we were not really any wiser for the evening's entertainment. Neither of our mothers spoke of it or even asked about it when we returned. Years later I reproached my mother for my prolonged state of ignorance.

'But I thought you knew,' she said. 'Didn't Mrs Broadbent . . . at school . . . when you left . . . I thought . . . '

I had been married for years but she was still too embarrassed to go into details.

Mrs Broadbent, the admirable headmistress of St Helen's, had indeed just before I left at eighteen given us a 'Leaving Talk'. We listened attentively at her feet on her drawing-room floor, but all that was readily comprehensible was the advice not to marry too early. This was good in its way even if it did not go far enough and more by luck than judgment I took it. The only advice my mother gave me, as a preparation for marriage, was: 'If you keep cheerful and learn to cook, no man will ever leave you.'

This maxim also turned out to be useful.

My mother and her sisters had been given the conventional education of their time at a small private school which sounded like Miss Pinkerton's famous academy in *Vanity Fair*. They all wrote beautiful rounded hands, regular, clear and unvaried, even in old age. They learnt to paint a little, to embroider and to play the piano and they acquired a certain amount of basic information, largely through learning by heart. They knew all the rivers of England, Scotland and Wales and some of the exports of foreign countries. Most of these facts came from *A Child's Guide to Knowledge*, a book of questions and answers such as:

'Q. What is petroleum?'
'A. A very inflammable mineral oil recently discovered in many parts of the world.'

and this mine of information I still possess. Thus they grew up knowing the Latin names of most plants, a little French, shockingly pronounced, the dates of the Kings and Queens of England, and a selected version of their activities. (My mother told me she had been at school for years before she realized that the historical facts which she was learning by rote had actually taken place.) From this unpromising education she somehow acquired enough knowledge to do *The Times* crossword puzzle from the time of its inception to her last conscious day. She was always an avid reader. All operations would stop so that she could read an out-of-date paper which had lined the shelf she was turning out, and she encouraged the habit of reading, sympathizing with me when I sneaked off with a book when I should have been otherwise occupied. She was fond of poetry and in the hope that we might share this love she read, so she later told me, almost nothing else while she was pregnant. What effect this had is not scientifically proved, but we grew up also loving the conventional rhythms of her choice, which she read to us until we could enjoy them for ourselves, and when we grew tired of Kipling, Tennyson, Longfellow, Keats and Shelley, we composed our own, for discrimination we had yet to learn. We made up yards of doggerel about everything which happened and in Jack my mother saw an undoubted future Poet Laureate.

Our choice to begin with was as wide as hers. It only had to be printed. There was a golden store in our father's leather-tooled prizes and Nelson's sevenpenny classics. Only Scott defeated us, then as now, alas! Every week we were given *The Rainbow* and some of our richer friends had *Puck* as well. This we borrowed. Later we took the admirable *Children's Newspaper*, but *Little Folks* was altogether out of our range, costing as it did a whole shilling. However sometimes we were lucky enough to borrow this also. *Comic Cuts* was considered vulgar and was banned in case our gentle minds should be polluted, but one of Jack's friends lent it to us and we read it in secret, with what dire results one cannot tell. All I remember is an endearing burglar in a striped jersey, who went around with a sack on his shoulder helpfully labelled SWAG. A short while ago I heard that a copy of this prohibited reading fetched a vast sum at Sotheby's.

Without the enlightenment of more permissive standards in advertising and conversation and given the reticence of our parents, it is not surprising that our generation remained, with exceptions, naively and dangerously ignorant. The penalty for this (or it could be the reward) was a longer period of childhood, so that we enjoyed more time without responsibility than the children of today – a space in our lives when all decisions were made for us and sex was still a three-letter word, and merely a grammatical problem. I had a comfortable feeling that life was outside my control and was so conditioned to the power of authority that this did not oppress me until suddenly THE WORLD, with all its excitements and sorrows and conflicts burst upon me at the ripe old age of seventeen. It was ushered in by my first dance; then there was a visit to a real play in a real London theatre in the EVENING. Although this was only *A Kiss for Cinderella* by James Barrie, who had himself never grown up, it was a marked step forward from the pantomime matinées at Drury Lane. Except for Lena Ashwell's admirable attempts to give schools a chance to enjoy the plays of

Shakespeare, an occasional visit to the Pierrots when we went to the sea, or an over-ambitious amateur performance of a Gilbert and Sullivan opera in the Baptist Hall by the Pinner Operatic Society, we had no knowledge of the living stage. There was, of course, no television and the films were silent. Even cinemas we visited so seldom that we were liable to be overcome by their realism. We thought that everything we saw was perfectly true and taking place before our very eyes. Pearl White was in actual danger of falling off a cliff or being run over by a train. Even the comedies could have a terrifying effect and the antics of Charlie Chaplin or the Keystone Cops sent shivers down our spines. Jack had nightmares for weeks after seeing *Sealed Orders*. He went with his friend Reggie and Reggie's parents and no one ever extracted from him the reason for his terror, but the name of the film we have never been able to forget.

At Worcester, where I was taken for a treat to the Electric Theatre by a visiting aunt, I caused confusion by screaming, 'Don't let him sit down! Please don't let him sit down!' The hero was about to be electrocuted in fearsome detail with the electric chair at the ready. Who says that films today are more horrifying?

Because our acquaintance with the theatre was so limited we remembered almost every word of the yearly pantomime, so that one merged into another and even today, over half a century later, we can laugh over the memories of Will Evans and Stanley Lupino as 'The Babes in the Wood', in a gigantic permabulator, waving enormous bottles and dummies, and when outsize safety pins were extracted from their bottoms and their cries subsided we nearly fell out of our seats. At Drury Lane there was a Harlequinade with its routine of a clown, a string of sausages, Harlequin in his spangles and a dancing Columbine, a ritual as necessary and familiar and also as incomprehensible as some aspects of our religious exercises.

Hamlet at the Old Vic, Jack Buchanan's elegance at the Adelphi, Sir Henry Wood's concerts at the now vanished Queen's Hall and *Tosca* at the Dresden Opera House, with

Fritz Busch wielding his baton, were all yet to come, making an impact so tremendous that it was worth the wait. A few years before my mother died I tried to tell her that her theories had been right. Because she did not believe in sophisticated pleasures at an early age, she had stored up an enormous and lasting delight, which is denied to her more experienced grandchildren.

She was amazed.

'But I had no theories,' she said. 'None at all. You would have gone to everything, been everywhere, if there had been enough money. Didn't you know?'

This, like many other things, I didn't know. I didn't realize that when our parents went off in such style to a concert or a theatre, leaving us behind, it was because they had been given a couple of tickets for failing shows by an acquaintance of my father's, who worked for a theatrical agency. In all their glory they joined a sparse audience of nurses and landladies, to watch plays which, for good reasons, no one wanted to see.

'I didn't really have any theories about bringing you both up,' my mother explained. 'Things weren't discussed in those days as they are now. No one tried to analyse anything. We just did our best from day to day. We wanted to send you both to good schools and there were moments when it was a bit of a job to make the money go round. There never seemed to be time to think about why or wherefore. If we hadn't been so hard up in those days, everything would have been different.'

Different possibly, indeed probably, but not better.

16

Lo! in the middle of the wood,
The folded leaf is woo'd from out the bud
With winds upon the branch, and then
Grows green and broad and takes no care,
Sunsteep'd at noon.

                              Tennyson

At one time there was talk, in view of my height and pallor, of letting me spend some months with my grandparents in Worcestershire, but this undreamt-of happiness was not to be. There was my education to consider for I was then due to leave kindergarten and start eight happy years at St Helen's, Northwood, where I was to be first a day-girl and later a boarder. So it became no more than something which a little pig's ears should not have overheard. A compromise was reached and it was decided that after the family fortnight was over I should always be allowed to stay on until the very end of the school holidays.

Long afterwards, when I was in my early twenties and found to have advanced tuberculosis, my mother told me she regretted this change of plan.

'You should have lived there for a year,' she lamented. 'We should have let you run wild.'

But at my grandmother's house, when they had all gone home and I was left, a lone child, made much of, I had no desire to be wild. Peace enveloped me like a cloak. There were no raised voices, no sudden comings and goings, no frenzied searchings for something which was lost – for our beloved mother was a great loser of vital trifles – no urgent flurries; no demanding father with standards higher than we could possibly attain.

My grandmother did not romp with us as our uncles and

cousins did, nor did she climb the hills as our grandfather and father did. Neither did she, like our aunts, play endless card games with us. She merely gave us lavishly of her time and with everyone gone a quietness settled on the house, so deep, so cosy, it was like her own soft embrace. Even the housekeeping was different. There were no quick rushes to the shops. Once a month the grocer drove up in his dogcart and was received in the dining-room with sherry and biscuits. His stay was long and so was his order – flour by the stone, sugar by the sack. Tins, which had already polluted my mother's housekeeping in London, were considered by my grandmother to be not only highly dangerous but immoral.

All was miraculously slowed down to a steady, regular pace where each day had its own rhythm and, as idleness was a sin, the hours were filled with unhurried busyness.

At the end of it, when I was fetched to go back to London, the presents I had made packed away in my suitcase, a pear given me at the last moment for the journey bulging in my pocket, the elastic of my hat tight under my chin, my mother would ask if I had been good.

'Very good,' my grandmother would say and, although my mother obviously found this difficult to believe, it was true.

My grandmother was one of those women, not intellectually clever, but full of a commonsense which only just falls short of wisdom, who are born to be wives and mothers and specially ordained by providence to be grandmothers. She had married at twenty and was then only in her early fifties, but in the clothes of the day she was already venerable, ageless and apparently permanent. In her photographs her figure makes her look a little like Mrs Noah.

This serenity, which was especially hers, was always protected and, to the day she died at the age of seventy-five, no one ever dared to let her open a telegram. News, good or bad, had to be broken to her with the greatest circumspection. Because she liked to do some of the cooking she was thought to be 'wonderful', and in comparison with her contemporaries she was indeed wonderful. Although she was never in a hurry she was never idle. Perched at her side on the special little chair, which had been my mother's, I learnt how to pod peas and broad beans and later I was allowed the adventure of holding a little knife, which came to be 'mine' and to cut scarlet runners and scrape new potatoes. We sat together in a summerhouse, which was cut out of a gigantic yew and we fitted into it so exactly that it was like wearing a huge aromatic tea-cosy. It was a romantic spot – hidden, sweet-smelling – which my grandmother occupied when it was fine.

On baking days I washed and dried the currants, stoned the raisins, pinched the skins of the soaked almonds to release the kernels, ate the sugar from the candied peel, weighed the flour, fetched and carried with no arguing or grumbles, sure of a lick of the bowl at the end. Each of our tasks she made into a private privilege.

In the afternoons she taught me to sew on buttons, to make moderately neat darns and to fabricate presents to take home – housewifes, needlecases, pincushions – a prodigious output of these resulted from the treasure chest which was her scrap bag. As these feminine skills were being inculcated, while we worked together she would recite ancient rhymes. 'A was an Apple Pie, B bit it, C cut it . . . ' ran through my head as I pricked my fingers and sucked the cotton. When I progressed to knitting and crochet she talked to me about her days at boarding school, showed me the teacaddy with a lock and key which she took with her and the pincers which she had to use to cut up the sugarloaf. She told me that the first thing she remembered learning was how to fold her crinoline into a neat roll when she went to bed. She was a serious woman and sometimes she talked of serious things, of the baby daughter who had died just before our mother was born, and how her grief had made her cry so much that our mother had been a sad child. I could not believe this of our cheerful mother. She told me of the wild riding and driving of her father, of how her sister, Mary Jane, a formidable spinster great-aunt, had been thrown out of the rear seat of the dogcart on their way back from school and had not been missed until they drove into the stableyard. She described how she jumped the tollgates and was often brought home on a hurdle. I did not know what a hurdle was but it explained her nervousness of horses and why we were not encouraged to ride.

Until Jack was born I was the only grandchild. Rose produced another grandson, John, when I was fifteen so that I was always her only granddaughter. Between us there was and remained an abiding bond. From the moment I could write a letter, until she died nearly twenty years later, we corresponded regularly. Every week, at home, at school and later in foreign countries and in hospitals, I would receive the news in her elegant spidery script on thick white paper, double-folded. She would hope I was being good and insert improving advice. More often that not she enclosed a little something, a brown packet of Peter's chocolate, a few stamps, a damp parcel of the first roses, a cutting from the local paper, a quotation, trite but true, like most platitudes. 'How poor are they who have not patience!' and 'There can be great happiness in a little house' are two which stick in my mind.

Her gentleness was part of the peace which surrounded her. When I was with her I did not argue, for there seemed to be no need. I accepted that my clothes must be mended and my thank-you letters written and my presents made. I accepted that the old woman in the cottage at the end of the coachhouse, who did our washing, should be given a plate of Sunday dinner and that I must take it to her, as I must carry a basket of tomatoes to the family at the end of the hopyard; that I must make the spills from old letters, collect the fir cones for the fire, top and tail the gooseberries. Errands, which at home were only undertaken after prolonged argument, were now performed with a skip and a jump before I was back with demands for more. With enthusiasm eggs were fetched from the farm at the end of the lane, the newspaper brought up from the corner, messages were borne, empty baskets returned to neighbours or full ones brought back. There was always something to do and yet time for the mind to wander.

All the houses within a quarter of a mile of the green could be reached by a honeycomb of footpaths and I skipped along them all. I knew where the blackberries and crab apples were to be found, where the stinging nettles were a dangerous hazard. I breathed the heady scent of the hops and sensed the thrill of danger overcome, when an adder was killed. I also learnt to pinch my nose when passing the Smell.

The Smell was caused by the inadequate drainage system of the entire neighbourhood and my grandfather, forecasting death from fatal diseases, had begun to complain about it from the time of Rose's birth. When he died fifty years later he was still complaining.

Most of all I liked being sent to the post.

The Lower Wick Post Office was the most sub of all sub post offices. It merely sold stamps and dealt with parcels and letters; telegrams had to be sent from farther afield, dog licences obtained from Worcester itself. Family allowances, pensions, television and wireless licences were the burdens of the future. Indeed, when the first Old Age Pension was granted – five shillings a week or twenty-five New Pence – some of its recipients could not be persuaded that it was not a personal benefaction of my grandfather's and he was overwhelmed by undeserved gratitude, which, however hard he tried, he could not convincingly explain away.

The Post Office was the front hall of an old red brick cottage, set in a large and prolific carden. The door stood open and inside the only signs of officialdom were two well-burnished pairs of brass scales, a big one for parcels and a fascinating and more exact one for letters, which had to be just so in case we were cheating the government out of a halfpenny. There was a grandfather clock standing on the shiny red flagstones and under a cloth on the small table was, as everyone knew, a key. After a time the postmistress arrived from the garden or the kitchen, often a little put out at being disturbed. She would lift the cloth, take out the key from its secret hiding place known to all and open the little drawer containing the stamps and the cash box. She did not

actually ask what was in the parcel or to whom it was being
sent or why, but by the time she had weighed it and the
stamps had been affixed, she knew. Even more remarkable,
in those days of the bicycle and the horse, the parcel would
arrive at its destination without fail on the following day.

Telegrams were another matter. To send them one had to
go to St John's and they were delivered by a much envied
smart boy in a pillbox hat and riding a bicycle. For sixpence
a dozen words could be sent and sometimes much brain
searching was necessary to keep within its limits so as not to
waste a word. Endearments were cut to a minimum, or if
necessary eliminated. In our family it was unheard of to have
anything to say which could not be compressed into twelve
words. One of the many things which later astounded me
about my in-laws' attitude to life was the fact that nobody
gave this mental exercise any attention.

Sometimes the dashing boy stood around eating an
apple and a piece of cake while we all wrestled with a
'Reply Paid'. Telegrams generally meant one of three things,
a birth, a death or that our father had missed his train.
Death had its own mysterious impact; birth was more
exciting. Our great-uncle at Witley sent a telegram announcing the arrival of the eldest, a letter for the second and
a postcard for the third. The births which followed, and
there were seven more of them, somehow lost their news
value and after that he waited until he had occasion to
drive into Worcester.

After Jack had gone I was allowed the heady privilege of
Staying Up To Supper, not to be considered while he was
still there in case it gave him ideas above his station, and
so it was that as dusk fell and the lamps were lit I was taught
to play whist, rummy and a bastardized bridge with all the
venom removed, while only the fun and mental exercise
remained. I learnt Solo, Nap and Cooncan, a game which
had been brought from America by one of my grandfather's relations, and there was an educational pack of
cards – a relic of our mother's childhood – called 'Counties

of England'. From this I acquired some basic geography which conveniently stuck.

On Sundays at my grandparents' none of these secular diversions was allowed, although at home I was permitted to knit and later on to sew. There the rot had set in when it was thought the standards might be bent for patriotic reasons to allow us to knit for our gallant soldiers in the trenches. From there the slide down the slippery slope was inevitable, until we actually even sewed. But this decline in our standards at home was never mentioned. It was all part of the giddy life we were supposed to lead in London. It was understood, however, that in our grandparents' house such goings-on could not take place and even to sew on a vital button was a sin. My grandmother never reduced her standards. For the last seven years of her life she was bed-ridden and playing Patience with herself and other card games with her visitors was a favourite diversion to while away the weary hours. On Sundays, however, the cards were stowed out of sight together with her embroidery, and she did not yield to our tempting persuasion.

At the end of every Sunday, when we went in to wish her 'Good night', she would look at her folded hands and sigh.

'It has been such a long day,' she would say.

In one of my novels, *Fair Shines the Day*, I described the life of a girl from the turn of the century to the uneasy peace between the wars. For the opening chapters my aunts supplied helpful details of their clothes, and a way of life which had overlapped into my own childhood scarcely changed. I thought my research was adequate, but when the book appeared I was swiftly informed of an error.

'No one would have played Ludo on a Sunday,' they said in shocked surprise. 'No one!' And I believed them. It was a regrettable oversight and I should have known better.

Although I am never conscious of putting myself into novels, my relations do not believe this. According to them, there I am alive and voluble on every page.

'So that's what she got up to in France,' I can hear them

saying. 'I always thought there was more in that dark school-master than met the eye.' Even my husband on reading my first book, *Come Lasses and Lads*, in the jungles of Burma (no less than thirty-six times because there was nothing else, as he so kindly informed me), sent me a frantic air letter demanding to know who the chap was whom I kissed in Chapter Twenty. All my long-distance denials failed to convince, but after reading this simple tale and returning home, where the choice was wider, he understandably read no more of my immortal works and his accusations ceased. Indeed few of my relations have read any of my books other than in the spirit of duty. They consider writing to be a strange thing to which I am addicted and as blood is thicker than water they bear with me in much the same way as they would have done had I been born half-witted or with a hare-lip or some other peculiarity. As a member of the family I must be supported, and they have been known, so I am told, to boast about me, but in my hearing their appreciation is muted. After supposed revelations of a doubtful past, mistakes are what delight them most and they pounce on misprints with the eye of a proof reader. Not that my friends and relations actually go to such lengths as to buy my books. With a few exceptions they expect free copies and until I became mean and cut off supplies I must have been my own best customer. Now they merely complain when my masterpieces are not thick on the public library shelves.

'Ask for them,' I reply, hardening my heart, and they write back: 'The librarian says she has never heard of you.'

Up For Sale

17

And one was rather mad
And all were rather trying
So little life they had,
So long they spent a-dying.

            Colin Ellis

In a welfare state of mass production and uniformity a certain amount of eccentricity seems to have disappeared, or have we ourselves, with the advancing years, become oddities to succeeding generations? Are we now regarded with the suppressed mirth or thoughts of sheer terror which visits to and from certain of our grandparents' friends engendered? Some of them we thought of as being merely slightly wanting and therefore harmless, like the old man who sat in front of us in church, putting on his gloves, slowly and with deliberation, and then with the same slowness and deliberation taking them off again. In between he would turn round and stare at us in a way which we had been told was impolite, but his watery, vacant eyes and his mild expression were so endearing that we smiled back. He was supposed to have been dropped by his nurse at an early age. Nurses must have been singularly careless, for this had happened as well to a pathetic but cheerful friend of Lily's, who had a hump. We tried not to be scared of her or even to notice it, but after reading *The Hunchback of Notre Dame* it was difficult, kind and amusing though she was.

There was also the man across the aisle in church, who sang half a beat behind us all in a fascinating manner. When he was no longer there the memory of him suddenly became frightening and even his empty pew made one draw one's breath, because we overheard the grown-ups' speculations as to how his drowned body came to be in the treacherous river Teme. Every year this tributary of the Severn, which ran near our grandparents' house, claimed its victims. It was a pretty river with seductive pools where the local boys bathed and fished and there was a salmon jump where, in dry spells, I paddled with the girls or lay in the sun to read and dream under the willows. But when there were storms in the Welsh upper reaches of the Severn the water came down the Teme with a fierce rush and flooded the ground floors of the Mill Cottages: it turned small eddies into whirlpools and spread across the Ham, making a little lake of the hollow where the Civil War soldiers were buried. The sinister depths of the mill race gave us a frisson of fear as we hung over the old walls. The battle of Powick Bridge had been fought there and we looked down with horror at the red water, even though we were assured that this was now due to the good red sandstone of the Worcestershire soil through which it wound its course, land known to generations of our forbears, from the days when the little bridge had been the only river crossing in these parts, before the making of the road over the 'New' Bridge, built to celebrate the Jubilee of Queen Victoria. There was always something alarming about the river Teme, whether in spate or so dry that there were tempting shallows and small gravel islands, and for once we found no difficulty in obeying our elders when they forbade us to bathe with the other children.

The man we most liked to hear about lived at Hivy Ouse. He became so tired of the mispronunciation of Ivy House that he changed the name officially and painted its mistakes with awful finality on the gate. He was the first person in the neighbourhood to own a car, and he drove up in a snorting monster filled with veiled women. He was also the first to take up photography and many of the pictures in the albums, beige and fading, of all the mob of our kith and kin, transformed into stern and unbending characters by the necessity of keeping still for the required number of minutes, were a testimony to his prowess. Sometimes in the corner a fuzzy blur depicts a child who was unable to survive the ordeal.

There seemed to me, in our childhood, to be an undue number of slightly dotty females who lived with even dottier companions. These we had, perforce, to visit. I cannot believe that they were any more pleased to see us than we were to see them, but it was understood that it had to be done and we consoled ourselves with the thought of their separate compensations, orchards where we could gorge until even our resilient stomachs were satisfied; ancient toys which were brought forth for our pleasure, a monkey on a stick, a musical box, a wooden doll, or perhaps a silver sixpence to take home. On one terrible occasion we were only offered pennies, and we refused. With the implacable indignation of negotiating trade unionists we stuck out for more. I can still remember the storm which broke when we returned home. Accusations of ingratitude, rudeness and other deadly sins were dinned into our rebellious ears. Jack as a small boy had a unique way of conveying that he was taking absolutely no notice.

'I am not looking and I am not listening,' he once said and although he never actually uttered these words a second time he continued not to look and not to listen. Even the back of his neck and the set of his ears made his feelings clear. My own opposition was always much noisier and more vehement and liable to end in tears but it was nothing like so effective as his silent protest.

One visit which was absolutely not to be avoided was to the heart of Worcester where in a quiet square our grandfather's cousin Polly lived with a browbeaten companion. She was a widow, her husband having been another cousin of my grandfather's, so there was a double relationship and a double duty. He had been a surgeon who early in his professional life had broken his arm while hunting and this had stiffened, thus giving him a welcome excuse for relinquishing his practice and following the example of his brother, Edward Bradley (Cuthbert Bede), in becoming an intermittent writer. I was told that he had dandled me on his knee, though I have no recollection of him or of this privilege, but his wife Polly, no dandler on knees, was unforgettable. Because of the cousinship they had no children. Why, and still less how, this was achieved was not, of course, explained to us and the house had that deadly chill of ordered tidiness which a childless home can, alas, produce. Polly Bradley never sat in an easy chair and she always wore black. She was the only person I remember who actually wore a lace cap and even as I write these words I wonder whether I have imagined this. Perhaps it was a spiritual lace cap which surrounded her head like an aura or a halo. She was a reputed 'character', later surviving a broken hip and spending years in a wheelchair with no loss of spirit. Her companion pushed her to church, to the little Theatre Royal, to the Three Choirs Festival, where she always sat in state blocking the aisles and making nonsense of other people's convenience or the fire regulations.

My mother and her sisters always enjoyed these visits to her but to us they were bleak indeed. When we arrived she would stare down at us from what seemed to be a great height. Then she would slowly lift up her voluminous black skirt to find a pocket situated in some dark insanitary recess of her petticoats. From this she would produce a bar of chocolate for each of us and we would be told to go into the garden and not to make a noise or to get ourselves dirty. The garden was a tiny walled strip at the back having access to a narrow lane. We always climbed the wall and sat on the top admiring the view. The wanton ruin of later 'developers' was not foreseen and even at that age I knew that to sit perched on high and looking across a medley of old roofs to the Cathedral towering above the Severn, with the everlasting hills beyond, was a satisfying experience. Everything was covered in soot from the neighbouring chimneys. Jack was inevitably in his tussore suit and I was in white muslin; moreover we each clutched in our hands a rapidly melting bar of chocolate. We might perhaps have managed to keep quiet but it was asking too much to expect us to keep clean.

The bathroom, where we were afterwards taken, with many chastening words, was itself memorable. There was a free-standing bath in the middle of acres of polished linoleum, a naked monstrosity with cast-iron feet, proudly planted with the same sturdy grandeur of the lions in Trafalgar Square. Today such objects are likely to be found in remote fields for watering cattle or in way-out collections of Victoriana. Everywhere smelt of lavender water and brass polish. Next door, at the top of the stairs, on a sort of half-landing, the lavatory was even more exciting. It was situated in a boxed throne, approached by two steps, and there was no plug to pull or lever to press, only a handle, difficult to manipulate without help. This had to be raised and lowered – clunk – clunk – from its shiny mahogany casing, while we were reproved for gazing with fascination at the beautiful pink roses which decorated the pan. Like so many of our activities this was, for some unexplained reason, considered to be 'rude'.

In 1849 my grandfather's uncle, Thomas Nightingale Avern, with his wife and children, one only a baby, set sail for America and in my great-grandmother's diary there is a note of their departure. 'May God go with them!' she wrote in pious hope.

Over a hundred years later, when my books were being considered for publication in the States, I received a long letter. 'Dear Cousin Margaret', it began. It was signed 'Your affectionate cousin, Elizabeth Avern Scott' and it contained a potted history of the intervening century. After many weeks in a sailing ship the little family had arrived safely, accompanied by their own goat, taken for the nourishment of the baby, who was the mother of the writer of the letter. Her grandfather, Thomas Avern, had in his baggage samples of needles from Redditch, the idea being that he should thereby make his fortune. It need hardly be said that he did no such thing. In fact my new-found relative still possessed the needles which were in mint condition. He had apparently just managed to establish himself in Atlanta, Georgia, when he was hit by the Civil War. In this he backed the wrong horse and his house was burnt, his wife died and he was left with a young son and a ten-year-old girl who was my cousin's mother. Her uncle was the Avern who had come to England at the beginning of the century to collect the money which was supposed to be in Chancery, returning to America with his pockets as empty as the rest of the family's. But from this strain emerged two American boys, both of whom fought in the Second World War. Tragically neither of them survived; one was killed and the other died of wounds, so now there was no one left with the name of Avern, with the exception of this new-found eighty-year-old cousin Beth, my mother's sister Lily and me. We had all been given it at our christenings. At long intervals we corresponded. She never sent her letters by air and our communications had the leisurely pace of another age. Eventually she sent me a small package of the pathetic treasures which had been taken out from England more than a century before by her grandparents ready for their new life – marriage lines, cuttings from the paper of their wedding, a small shield with a coat of arms roughly carved upon it, which she said came from a piece of wood off the family estate. It was news to me that we possessed such a thing as a coat of arms, still less an 'estate', but I dutifully hung it over our old fireplace, and meant, as the months went by, to check its authenticity. But it has not been done. When I do get down to making proper enquiries I should not be surprised to find that it is based on the purest fantasy. Half of me never quite believes the old stories, though it would be pleasant to do so. When I wrote to my American cousin with some scepticism of these legends, suggesting that our name Avern, if really derived from the French, was not Norman at all but possibly of humbler Huguenot origin, I was reproved six weeks later in no uncertain terms. She had been brought up in the firm belief, she wrote, that she was of Norman descent and she was not going to change her mind. Moreover she maintained that the Nightingale in her grandfather's name connected us, how, she did not specify, with the famous Florence. Our letters covered many topics, from the harvest of peccan nuts in her 'backyard' to politics, and I was often amazed to find that her opinions

were more reactionary than any British Capital C Conservative. Her views on the colour problem would have set
the Race Relations Board on fire. Long dissertations on the
iniquities of the Kennedy family, whom she regarded as Irish
revolutionary upstarts, covered page after page, round the
edges and along the margins, using every inch to propound
viewpoints which one would have thought had Gone With
The Wind. A few years ago she wrote that she was ill, and
then the letters stopped.

When I looked up the names of the Knights who fought
with William the Conqueror at the Battle of Hastings I was
amazed to find one called AWERNE.

18

Every second is a kind of rich nostalgia.

Elizabeth Jennings

Anne Edwards in her column in the *Sunday Express* once wrote that the best parents a child could possess must be loving, with a reverence for education, and they must also be hard up. All three qualifications, in my early years, our parents undoubtedly possessed. Jack, being younger than I, remembers less of the difficult years, for by the time he had reached his teens some of my father's ambitions had been achieved, but his recollections, though vaguer than mine, have apparently the same basis.

'What do you remember most clearly?' I asked him recently.

'Nothing special,' he said. 'Just being happy.'

Yet although at that time children were not actually being sent down the mines, it was an era of bad conditions and unemployment, but my father, remembering the hardships of his own youth, was, in his day, considered to be a good employer, holding advanced views. There were official tea-breaks in his factory and offices long before such things became taken for granted or even abused. He instituted pensions, a social club and paid holidays and, because his factories began from nothing and remained comparatively small, he knew all the people who worked for him. When he needed extra effort he explained why and they responded. He knew the names of their children, where they lived and how they lived and we grew up knowing this too.

'Never forget,' he would say, 'the people who work for me help to give you all the things you have.'

He was strict and he was tough and worked so hard himself that he did not always understand how others, including his own family, might be less dedicated, not least my brother to whom he was, perhaps, over-meticulous in showing no favours. When Jack's time came he had to work as hard or even harder than everyone else just because he was the son of the boss. Yet although his standards were high my father always had a deep concern and affection for everyone whom he employed.

When the young wife of one of them died of the disease which was then afflicting me, they sympathized with each other in their troubles. They knew about us just as we knew about them. After the factory was moved out to Buckinghamshire he helped with removals and resettlements. For the first time in their lives some now had gardens and my mother would have long discussions with them about their gardening problems and they would exchange plants and wail about the weather and the poor stony soil with which they all wrestled. My enlightened friends now tell me that this was paternalism and an evil thing. Perhaps so, but at the time it did not seem evil. It was still an era of small undertakings and the bigger and better, but not necessarily brighter, factory units have lost something in their development, something indefinable and maybe precious. Between my father and his employees there was a bond of tolerant affection on both sides. They respected him and as he grew older they were more patient with him than he was with them. They also appreciated him and some of them, who had worked for him for such a long time that they were part of the equipment and had known Jack and me all our lives, had for him a deep understanding.

He liked to hear of the progress of their children and a few years ago, when Jack was enquiring about the health of a pensioner, he was told with pride of the successes of his children and grandchildren. They had all done well and he was justifiably proud of them.

'I wish the Governor was still alive,' the old man said. 'I'd have liked to have told him.' Then he added, 'He'd have been so pleased.'

In the Second World War, when he was an old man, my father and a few other old men kept things going by prodigious efforts.

It was ironic and perhaps a portent for the future that when he had not enough petrol for his car he was turned off a bus which served the neighbouring factories.

'This is for THE WORKERS,' the conductress said, eyeing his briefcase and trilby hat.

He was left standing in the road roaring with laughter. Then he set off to walk the two miles home, hurrying, for he could not wait to share the joke, as he shared everything with my mother.

He was generous in a rare way. He gave without thought of reward and then he forgot. I never heard him utter those fatal words which negate all giving: 'And after I did so much for them . . . '

In some people generosity is a form of vanity. They give partly to glorify themselves. This was not his way. He was often more generous than he could afford to be but to do this he denied himself. An unpaid bill was to him the same as stealing. Once when we were grown-up and all dressed up to be taken out by him he told us of an old account book which he had found. In it was an entry of his youth: 'On the bust – one shilling'. Looking at us in all our glory he laughed and we laughed with him. But we should have cried.

Now that I, too, am old I can hate myself for my own lack of gratitude, for so pitifully little was spent on himself. Most of the results of his labours went to provide a good life for us, to educate us and later to pay my enormous doctor's bills; to give help to others when it was needed, often in ways that were not known, and to make our lives, after he had gone, easier than his own had been.

Because he had found his insular upbringing and lack of

languages a disadvantage in the new Central European states thrown up by the Treaty of Versailles, where his further business interests now took him, he was determined that his children should not be so handicapped. In his late forties he had tried to learn German himself, studying Berlitz manuals and attending classes after long days at the office. But his tired brain rebelled, for although he was a good Latin scholar he only absorbed enough of the language to recognize, when I later had to act as his interpreter, that my translations were sometimes more inspired than accurate. Jack was also a good Latin scholar and his exact mind was like his father's. He also learned German, not so quickly as I did, but much more accurately and with better results. After the First World War it was not easy for me to be allowed to take German lessons at school to prepare me for later studies abroad. My admirable headmistress thought that only French was socially acceptable and this was brilliantly taught. I actually left school able to speak French, a rare feat in those days when 'School French' was a language set apart and only comprehensible to another Englishman. Some of my parents' friends shared her objection to German and they wrote imploring my father not to send me to Dresden.

Never easy to persuade, he resisted.

'If you want to hate your enemies,' he said, 'it is better to understand what they say and hate them, if you must, in their own language.'

Jack and I are now grateful for the sacrifices both our parents made so that we could learn languages. It opened a window on the world, useful in many circumstances and places.

In the thirties, on our honeymoon, my husband sent his new parents-in-law a postcard from the Black Forest.

'Margaret's German has saved me so much money', he wrote, 'that I shall be forced to retain her services.'

My father was an uncertain man but my mother was always the same. She had no moods other than an apparent calm benevolence and I was middle-aged before I realized that this misleading serenity often hid deep anxieties. With our father we had to choose our moments. There were days when you could tweak his tail and days when you could not even stroke him. But though he was undemonstrative he was loving, the contradictory result of the lack of affection in his own childhood. To the very end he liked to be hugged and made a fuss of, even though he would look over his glasses and say: 'And what is it that you want, h'm?' for he liked to pretend that we were really out for what we could get, knowing full well that if this had been so his shrewd eyes would have instantly seen through us. But when we really wanted anything we went first of all to our mother. She paved the way. Yet there was no mistaking who was in charge. It was my father. At least my mother let it be thought that he was always, as Elsie called him in the manner of those days, 'The Master'. Perhaps this power of deception on our mother's part that he was boss was her greatest quality and when success eventually came to him, he was the first to admit that without her he would have achieved nothing.

Sometimes as I grew older, I wondered how she could remain unmoved by his sudden outbursts of irritability.

'I understand him better than you do,' she said, 'and it's a good thing he's a bit difficult. If he'd had charm as well he would have been devastating.'

As it was she had no problems with 'other women' for there was none. He once said to me: 'Faithfulness was easy. I never was even tempted. I never clapped eyes on anyone half as wonderful as your mother.'

He did not retire until he was over seventy and I think that all his working life he must have been over-tired, for when the burden was lifted, much against his will, he at last seemed to relax and he became mild, even gentle; but though no longer irritable he remained demanding. He was used to his own way, and our mother had undoubtedly spoilt him. When we told her this she would agree, and then add: 'He's so good to me. He has always been – so good to me,' but it was she who was good to him. Perhaps they were good to each other; more than that, they were right for each other, and in being so they were right for us, their children.

This was, and remained even after they were both gone, our unforgettable good fortune.

19

Grave men, near death, who see with blinding sight . . .

Dylan Thomas

When my mother died a few weeks after their Golden Wedding my father said an odd thing. In the first few months after her death, when we were deeply concerned with what steps should or could be taken to make his life as happy and comfortable as was possible alone, we discussed the endless problems of selling or not selling the house; of where to go and what to do. Having seen his own sister and sister-in-law give up their lives to their parents, he was adamant that he would be no such burden to us. Yet his own misery was itself a burden merely to watch as he considered the disposal of his home and the treasures acquired by his hard work and perspicacity, trying with much courage to adjust to life without her.

It was then that he made this strange remark.

'If she were only here,' he said, 'I could get through it. When she was with me I could always get through things, however bad they were, and if she were here now I could get through this.'

In every crisis she had been at his side and that he now needed her to help him through the trauma of her own death did not strike him as nonsense or inconsistent. Nine months later he also was dead. He caught a cold and he died. It was totally unexpected, for although he was eighty he was a strong man, and with modern drugs no one was allowed to succumb to the mercy of death by pneumonia.

But for him they were of no avail. He shut his eyes and he died.

'It was a broken heart,' said a friend and we could only agree, nor did we wish our father back to live in a world which, despite all our efforts, was now irrevocably desolate.

At the time of my mother's death two things happened which shook my avowed disbelief in the supernatural.

Jack's elder daughter was then four years old and my mother's brief illness, following a stroke, was kept from her. She was merely told that Granny was ill and could not see her until she was better, though she may well have overheard more than we imagined. She was and is, in some ways, very like her grandmother and, as a much-longed-for first grandchild she was especially loved.

The day before her death my mother lay unconscious. I have often wondered just how aware of their surroundings unconscious people really are, knowing that once when I was near death myself I knew that people were speaking to me and about me and yet I felt too weak and far away to answer. Be that as it may, we were told that our mother's death was near.

A few miles away Isabel was playing with her baby sister. It was a heavy day in early summer and there was thunder in the air. Suddenly the child stood quite still looking into a corner of the hall, dark because of the storm.

'Someone is over there,' she called.

Her mother, Joyce, a practical woman of great commonsense, was nevertheless chilled by the thought that her mother-in-law must be dead, and Isabel was seeing a ghost.

'Who is it?' she asked.

'It's Granny,' said the child.

'Then wave to her,' said Joyce, as calmly as she could, and the child waved obediently into the dark corner.

'Goodbye,' she said, and then as she turned back to her toys she added, 'She's gone now.'

It was not until the early hours of the following morning that her grandmother died. Did she in her last hours project her loving spirit into her grandchild's presence for a last farewell, or was the child playing an imaginary game? Perhaps it was only a fancy, for today she remembers nothing of the incident.

Five days later, on the morning of the funeral, something else strange happened.

My father's youngest brother, Fred, had, intentionally or otherwise, to some extent cut himself off from the rest of his family, and my mother's own family were such a devoted unit that she had always deplored this.

'I only see Fred at funerals,' she used to say.

When she was taken ill I had come to look after my father. It was the first death with which I was personally concerned and, apart from my own sadness, I was anxious about many things. I was worried about my father's state of misery and how I was to get him through the day; I was worried about his future and I was also concerned about the mundane matter of the funeral baked meats. The inevitable relations were coming to lunch before the funeral and to tea afterwards, and they had to be fed. My mother was much in my mind as I busied myself in her kitchen, trying helplessly to take her place. I took up my father's breakfast and on the tray was a letter from his brother, Fred, announcing that he, too, was coming to the funeral.

'That would have amused her,' he said, and for the first time in weeks he gave his one-sided smile, but when I came back to fetch the tray I was alarmed to see him staring wide-eyed across the room.

'I've just seen your mother – over there – ' he said, pointing to the door, 'and she was laughing.'

I thought that the strain had affected his mind and found myself saying, in a there-there nurse-like voice, 'Well, perhaps she knows that Uncle Fred is coming to the funeral.'

He agreed and settled back on his pillows with his eyes closed, and I carried the tray out of the room, feeling very disturbed. Half-way down the stairs I heard a bellow from the hall.

'I stayed the night at the Royal, so I've come good and early,' said a man's unmistakeable voice.

It was Uncle Fred.

20

*Man's days are like the grass, he blossoms like the flowers
of the field. A wind passes over them and they cease to be
and their place knows them no more.*

New English Bible

Although I have lived in many places, both at home and
abroad, it is Worcestershire which seems to claim an
affectionate allegiance. Yet only a few weeks in each year
of childhood were spent there before, by choice and circumstance, we all began to spread our wings. But we were still
drawn back for fleeting visits. Then, in 1940, the time came
for greater separations. We had passed through the uncertain stage of the so-called 'phoney' war and now we had
to say goodbye to our men who were leaving us, some for
the Far East, which in those days really was far, or for the
other east which was called near, or for that last abortive
fight in France, before Dunkirk, or perhaps to fly in the sky
for our protection. We saw the evacuees fleeing out of our
bombed towns, the refugees arriving from the countries over-
run by the enemy and for the first time we began to perceive
dimly that we ourselves might be invaded. Defeat was something we never envisaged but we wondered if in some future
nameless confusion, difficult to contemplate, we might too
lose touch and have to search despairingly for each other, as
the French and the Poles were searching.

As always it was Dick, my husband of three years' standing,
who had the foresight and the ideas. 'We must all make for
one focal point,' he said. 'There must be a place where we
can all go, sometime, at the end, no matter what happens –
a clearing house where we can all find each other.'

The only place which came to our minds was the old house at Lower Wick in the very heart of England. Why we should think it would necessarily survive in such an uncertain future as we contemplated remains a mystery, but the thought that it existed gave us all a feeling of security, when we watched each other vanish into the unknown. Now that both her parents were dead Lily lived there alone, defended by a man's hat hung in a prominent position in the hall to discourage tramps. A pillar of the church and the Women's Institute, she sacrificed the tranquillity of her old age to the Second World War, as she had given up her youth for the First. Indefatigable, for over six years of war, she worked in a factory and for the Red Cross; dug for victory, housed evacuees and landgirls, and nursed us at intervals when required. Then one day, when it was all over and we had settled down to enjoy the spurious pleasures of the so-called peace, she announced that she could no longer stay there.

'I only kept it for you all,' she said, and now she knew that we had other lives and other ties and Rose's son, John, who had loved it most of all and had planned to live there in his old age, was cruelly paralysed with multiple sclerosis.

'It must be sold,' she said.

As usual her voice was firm, her mind made up and not to be swayed.

All her life had been spent in the old house but, without a backward glance, she packed a few treasures and left to help Rose in nursing the invalid John. To Jack and me fell the task of dismantling it. Except for the installation of electricity and a hot-water system, nothing appeared to have been changed. Nothing had apparently been thrown away either; it was in apple-pie order but it was all there, the stereoscope, the faded family groups, Uncle Willie's Little Jokes, our mother's dolls' house, now in sad disrepair, and the pictures of the Infant Samuel, whose artistic merits my father had so often derided. The framed text: 'Foxes have holes, birds have nests, but the Son of Man hath not where to lay his head' still hung in the room I regarded as 'mine'. It had always given me a sensation of chilling sadness as I lay facing it, cosy in my warm feather bed. There still lingered in the huge larder – itself bigger than most modern kitchens – an aroma of all those gargantuan feasts for the gatherings of friends and relations, the weddings, the anniversaries, the christenings and the funerals.

Without the wisdom and hard work of Jack's wife, Joyce, we should doubtless have left it as it was. She brought us down to earth and with reluctance we became practical. Some things we kept and some we sold and some we gave away; some went to Jumble Sales; some ended in museums and some in the dustbin. In deciding what fell into which category we made sad mistakes, as we afterwards found. Indeed Lily herself, that dedicated hoarder, had given into the maw of 'salvage' during the war a collection of old magazines which were later found to be valuable numbers of *Household Words*, containing the original serial instalments of the novels of Charles Dickens.

A daunting task faced us. There were crinoline frames in tidy rolls, bustles, a laced stomacher made of strawberry-coloured velvet and an embroidered waistcoat with a ticket attached, mysteriously saying in brown faded ink, 'The Queen admired this'. There were curtains which had been bought in the Crimean War. They were of wool with threads of silk, once red, now faded to the colour of weak tomato soup and still used by Jack's younger daughter, Jo. Everywhere we turned we saw an imprisoned microcosm not only of our own childhood but of the childhood of the three women, whose home it had always been. In a box, all coiled and tied in case they 'came in', were several dog-leads and during the half-century when I had known the house there had never been a dog. They crumbled at a touch as if they had been removed from an Egyptian tomb, so that nothing was left but the dust of the past, known and unknown.

For us the house had always been a summer refuge, with sun streaming through the windows and tea on the lawn, but now it was November and bitterly cold. Lily had always scorned adequate heating. The cedar under which we used to sit had grown, giving the house an unfamiliar darkness and the trees in a nearby hedge blocked out the view of the

Malvern Hills. The house itself might be unchanged but it stood in totally different surroundings. The fields and orchards, where we had played, were filled with the bungalows of a new housing estate; the Post Office was on the main road, less handy but new and efficient with a telephone box and a shop, and the iron gate with its welcoming squeak, through which we had all surged to be swept into loving arms, had been taken away in 1943 to make weapons of war. Only the ruts and the mud in the lane, about which our grandfather and Lily had fought a losing battle from the beginning of the century, remained unaltered.

The coachhouse and stables which Lily had always talked of converting into a flat, and the cottage mysteriously joined on at the back – maybe the original 'cottage in the fields' on the old maps – had always made the north side of the house a jumble of roofs and gutters. As we examined its awkward deficiencies with the surveyor it seemed to ramble on and on, a nightmare of inconvenient and ill-conceived additions, and it was the only part which appeared to be bigger than I remembered, for everything else had shrunk. The green where Pierce had turned his horses with such a flourish looked no bigger than a postage stamp. Its smallness seemed to enclose all the day-dreams of childhood, when the joys and sorrows of the future were hidden. Many dire fates had been predicted for me, from Hell Fire to Reform Schools, but that I should spend years in sanatoria and be expected to die before I was thirty was not foreseen.

Neither was it foreseen that I should survive.